Contemporary Structure in Architecture

Leonard Michaels M.A., A.R.I.B.A.

Reinhold Publishing Corporation

330 West 42nd Street, New York, U.S.A.

To the memory of

my dear friend and father-in-law

GEORGE GERSON FREUDENSTEIN

in appreciation of many things.

Foreword

by Eric Mendelsohn

Recent developments in the knowledge of steel and reinforced concrete have confirmed the visions of the structural and architectural pioneers of contemporary building.

Both POST AND BEAM — the ancient static principle, and BUTTRESS AND VAULT — the medieval dynamic principle, are being superseded by the elastic principle of continuity of our time.

Both the static and dynamic principle resulted in structures invented by man, whereas the principle of Elasticity is dictated by Nature. Upon it Nature works in all her organisms; in her material, vegetable and animal kingdoms; in man, plant and atom. This is the structural meaning of "organic" architecture.

The revolutionary knowledge of the material nature and structural potential of steel and reinforced concrete, of methods and design, of practical application and architectural evaluation, is of utmost importance to all practitioners—to Engineers and Architects alike.

To be creative, the Architect must be the spiritus rector of all tectonic conditions: use, structure and form; to create his building as an organism — self-contained and in its kind — the structural idea must come from him.

To take his rightful place in this creative art, the Engineer, beyond his scientific computations, must be as sensitive to form as the Architect to structure—the only way for structure and form to challenge each other.

Mr. Michaels' survey—in its concise text and precise illustrations—makes comprehensible this organic relation between contemporary structure and architecture.

To our University Departments and students the study of this book is imperative; even to those who believe in and rely upon their structural vision and organic instinct, this book is enlightening.

Postscript to Foreword

by Prof. R. A. Cordingley

Mr. Mendelsohn's views accord almost precisely with my own. Structural science has made such headway in recent decades that the architect, structural engineer and all those concerned with the devising of building projects, are faced with an almost bewildering variety of constructive systems from which to choose. Yet the choice is not free; each type of system has its own special pertinence to particular classes of problem, and sound selection in any given instance is in fact governed by the suitability of a system on all counts of utility, adaptability, initial and long-term economy, maintenance costs, and, last but by no means least, permanently good appearance.

Latterly then, the need has been rapidly growing for a reliable exposition presenting a relative account of the whole range of alternative constructive systems, and appraising the suitability of each for particular circumstances and occasions; and when some time ago as a professional examiner, I had the pleasure of reading the early draft on which this book was built (in the form of a thesis presented by the author, already a Master of Arts in the University of Cambridge, in connection with

his professional diplomas in Architecture at the Regent Street Polytechnic, London),
it instantly appealed to me as meeting just this need. In its final shape this volume
gives, as nearly as one may hope in human affairs, an impartial evaluation of the
various systems, classified systematically according to an evolutionary pattern of
structural forces, and examined in general and in particular, sufficiently to show the
circumstances under which each can function with optimum efficiency and to highest
aesthetic advantage. The last aspect is all too rarely adequately considered in relation to industrial and commercial buildings, but good appearance is just as essential
to the maximum fulfilment of function as observance of prime utility. The book
should assist designers, not excepting professional students, to refresh their knowledge of the true values of the respective systems and to choose appropriately with
the maximum expedition and without danger of sacrificing logic to current,
evanescent fashion.

PREFACE

With the knowledge of technics and science developed far beyond the mastery of any one man, the architect has become essentially a co-ordinator of specialists. If he is to retain his creative role this co-ordination must be made active and not passive, for architecture can live only as a fountain-head which nourishes these specialists and not merely as a reservoir collecting and distributing their streams of thought and knowledge. The architect must therefore aim at knowing sufficient of the principles of each specialized subject on which his design depends, to enable him to lead and not to follow, to demand and not merely to acquiesce. Of all specialists, the engineer is the most vital to the architect since it is his work which turns creative imagination into concrete reality. Although there has been closer collaboration between architect and engineer in recent years, this in itself is insufficient, for the independent training of each, which mostly prevails, does not provide the essential mutual understanding of the principles and problems governing each other's work.

In this book, I have endeavoured to bridge the gap between the way of thinking of architect and engineer, a gap which *must* be bridged if architecture is to take full advantage of the revolutionary development of contemporary structure, and not regard it merely as a means of taking greater liberties with the forms arising out of structural principles no longer employed. I need not elaborate further upon the nature of the book, since this is made clear in the Foreword and Postscript, to the authors of which I am greatly indebted for their contributions. I have found it convenient to consider first, the complete range of contemporary structure, in order to place in true perspective the architectural potentialities of structural materials and the structural vocabulary which confronts the architect to-day. The subsequent analysis of the effects and influence of contemporary structure on the trends of architectural design, can then be followed with this structural vocabulary as a background, drawing upon it as necessary for the illustration of developments and potentialities.

I should like here to meet one possible criticism. This book is concerned with structural potentialities in relation to architectural design; with what *has* been done and what *can* be done within the limits of reasonable economy. An architect does not often seek the cheapest method of construction without having regard to other factors such as appearance, maintenance, durability, etc., and cost has therefore not been a criterion in selecting the structures illustrated; for if it had been, the scope of the book might have been much more limited. I have also avoided, as far as possible, the question of relative cost since this is bound to vary not only from one country to another and from one locality to another, but also from one decade to another or even from year to year. On the other hand, I have endeavoured to indicate methods of economising in material, which if not always leading to an overall saving in cost at the present time, seem to provide a sound basis for seeking economy.

A work of this kind would not be complete without reference to the structural materials on which the whole subject of the book depends. An understanding of the nature of these materials and the developments which have taken place both in their properties and in the methods of using them, is really a pre-requisite for the full appreciation of much of the material contained in the book. It has only been possible within the scope of this work, to provide comparatively brief surveys of the important materials of contemporary structure, and at the same time, since they are rather supplementary to the main subject matter, I have thought it best to introduce these surveys as an Appendix which can be consulted as required.

This book grew out of a desire on my own part to clarify the seemingly haphazard relationship which I felt to exist between structure and architectural design. One of the most difficult problems which I encountered when I came to write the early draft, was to decide the form in which the book should be built, and I am indebted to Mr. D. C. H. Jenkin at that time on the architectural staff of the Regent Street Polytechnic, London, for his useful suggestions in this matter. I am also grateful to Mr. Eric Mendelsohn of the University of California and to Professor R. A. Cordingley of the University of Manchester, England, for the very great interest which they have shown in seeing this book published.

The original draft has been considerably revised and enlarged to include many recent structures of outstanding interest. I am greatly indebted to Mr. Felix J. Samuely, Consulting Engineer of London, for reading through the original manuscript and for suggesting improvements designed to ensure that the work of an architect should be technically correct in the eyes of the engineer. I must also thank Mr. Ove N. Arup, Mr. O. Bondy and Dr. K. Hajnal-Konyi, all Engineers of London, for their kind cooperation and helpfulness.

The nature of the illustrations in this book, has involved the collection of photographs from many different countries in all parts of the world. A considerable number, however, had to be collected in the U. S. A. and in spite of the very great cooperation which I have received from United States architects, engineers, contractors, journals and other organisations, I could never have achieved so much success in tracking down certain illustrations, had it not been for the invaluable assistance of Mrs. Greta Wimpfheimer, who worked most efficiently and tirelessly on my behalf from New York City. In addition, I am indebted to Mr. Henry Kahn, news correspondent of Paris, for his very generous assistance in obtaining photographs from France. To my secretary, Mrs. Edith Greene, my thanks are also due for her faithful support in dealing with the unexpectedly large amount of correspondence resulting from the collection of all these illustrations. To my wife my thanks cannot be adequately expressed for her constant assistance, patience and support.

I am greatly indebted to the many people who have so kindly cooperated either in giving or lending photographs and other illustrative material, or in giving helpful information. The detailed acknowledgments will be found in the list of illustrations. In certain cases, however, photographs have been given or lent by persons or organisations other than those by whose courtesy they are reproduced. For such photographs I am indebted to: Architects, Walter Gropius of Harvard University, Marcelo, Milton & Mauricio Roberto of Rio de Janeiro, G. P. Dubois and J. Eschenmoser of Zurich, J. O'Hanlon Hughes of Dublin, Konrad Wachsmann of New York City; Engineers, Pier Luigi Nervi of Rome, Felix J. Samuely, Ove N. Arup, O. Bondy, Brian Colquhoun & Partners of London; Contractors, Holloway Brothers, Ltd., 'Twisteel' Reinforcement Ltd. of London; The Architectural Press Ltd., Cement and Concrete Association, British Iron and Steel Federation, The Royal Institute of British Architects, Swiss National Tourist Office, all of London; The Museum of Modern Art,

The American Institute of Steel Construction of New York City; The Portland Cement Association of Chicago.

Finally, I wish to say that I have, as far as possible, attached the names of architects and engineers to the captions of illustrations, but it has not been practical to obtain this information in all cases. In apologising for omissions, I invite any architect or engineer who can assist in completing the gaps, to inform either myself or the publishers, and such additional names as may be submitted, will be gladly added in future editions.

I conclude with the hope that this work will stimulate the forces of contemporary architecture, and lead to a greater understanding and harmony between engineer and architect.

London, February, 1950

Leonard Michaels.

TABLE OF CONTENTS

List of Illustrations and Acknowledgments

Contemporary Structure in Architecture

I.

Contemporary Structure

Structure, the primary function of which is the collection of loads and transfer of them to the ground, is represented in architecture between the two extremes of the multi-storey building with emphasis on load transfer and the large span single-storey building with emphasis on load collection. The scope of structure, however, is also bound up with the degree to which it satisfies the ultimate end of building, namely space enclosure. The development of the skeleton frame in the last 50 years has been accompanied by steady progress in the evolution of load carrying elements, which will serve the dual purpose of structure and space enclosure. This has been brought about by a new conception of contemporary structural materials, whose early use had been governed by the linear conception of timber, the only previous material which could be used in bending. The earlier examples in architectural history of the carrying over of forms from one material to another, have shown the copying of characteristic details of the old material, such as the Egyptian reeded column and the Greek orders, but the influence of timber on the development of steel and reinforced concrete seems to have been in conception rather than in detail. Maillart, the Swiss engineer, has said that "the engineer was so accustomed to using those basic materials which provide only one-dimensional support that they became second nature to him and restrained him from exploiting other possibilities." By his insight into the nature of reinforced concrete, Maillart played a decisive part in the development of the two-dimensional structural element, the plane or slab, to be followed later by the three-dimensional conception of shell construction, deriving the maximum strength from the material employed, by means of appropriate structural shape.

The Torengebouw, Antwerp, left, the highest building in Europe when completed in 1931, employed complex riveted connections to obtain rigid joints between beams and columns. (Architect: A. Vanhoenacker.)

3

Fig. 1, left, war damaged building in Gresham Street, London, erected about 1862 reveals internal framework of cast iron columns and steel beams contained within the external load-bearing walls.

Part 1
THE SKELETON FRAME

The skeleton frame, used so successfully in the past in spite of the severe limitations of available materials, received a new impetus with the development of the new tensile materials. The introduction of steel as a structural material opened up the field of vast spans and great heights by the concentration of loads in members whose cross-section was small compared with the structure as a whole. Since the early developments, this great concentration of forces in single structural members has given rise, as might be expected, to a great variety of methods of arranging the forces within the members, either by means of suitable structural shape or by varied arrangements of the components of individual members. In addition, the use of self-supporting skeleton frames, often of considerable height, has introduced the problem of lateral forces into the assembly of the skeleton itself.

Fig. 2, left, complex riveted connections to obtain rigid joints between beams and columns used in Torengebouw, Antwerp, shown in frontispiece.

Jointing

The scope and flexibility of the structural frame is closely bound up with the way in which the individual members are assembled to form the structure. In the early use of cast-iron and steel as a means of internal support (fig. 1), jointing was not of much importance since lateral forces were resisted by the enclosing masonry walls stiffened by the floors. Indeed under the Building Regulations in force in London in 1894, it was not permissible to fix the ends of beams to their supporting columns, as provision for expansion had to be made; it was only relaxation of this requirement which permitted the erection in London of the Ritz Hotel in 1904 with a complete steel skeleton. Triangulation, such as is used in a lattice girder, is the simplest method of obtaining rigidity, and although this is used both in single-storey and in multi-storey construction as a method of resisting lateral forces, it is often incompatible with the architectural requirements, especially in the case of multi-storey buildings where the lateral forces are the most severe.

The other method lies in the strengthening of the joints; and connections designed to resist the lateral forces of wind and earthquake have been used in the U.S.A. and elsewhere for many years. More recently there has been a tendency towards the development of rigid composite members designed in such a way that erection joints can be simplified by placing them where the minimum stresses occur. The idea of mutual support and continuity in framing members is the beginning of the road towards the monolithic shell. To the engineer, it means, except in the case of a three-hinged arch, a "statically indeterminate" structure which is more complicated to analyse than a "statically determinate" pin-jointed structure, but to the architect, it means greater possibilities in design.

Rigidity of the structural frame

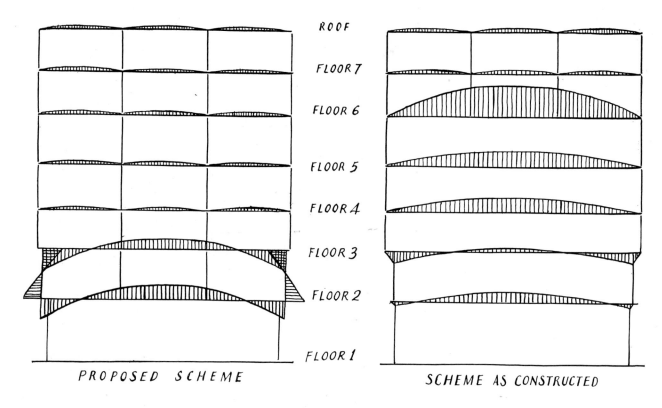

ROOF

FLOOR 7

FLOOR 6

FLOOR 5

FLOOR 4

FLOOR 3

FLOOR 2

FLOOR 1

PROPOSED SCHEME

SCHEME AS CONSTRUCTED

COMPARISON OF BENDING MOMENT DIAGRAMS

Continuity in construction

Recent research has confirmed that the traditional method of designing multi-storey steel frames as pin-jointed structures regardless of the moment connections employed to resist lateral forces, is far from the actual state of affairs, and that in fact varying degrees of rigidity are obtained, so that a load on one member produces some effect on all the others. Although the monolithic nature of reinforced concrete has long been recognised, the design of steel structures for continuity is a more recent development closely connected with progress in the technique of welding. It was possible, of course, to obtain rigid connections by means of riveting, as seen in fig. 2, which shows a specially designed riveted joint employed in the "Torengebouw" at Antwerp, which was the highest building in Europe when completed in 1931. This connection provided partial fixity to the beams, but was a very laborious process when compared with an equivalent welded joint, and occupied considerably more space. The significance of a wider acceptance of continuity design is well illustrated by the case of the proposed scheme for the use of restrained plate girders on the Piccadilly front of Simpson's Store, London (fig. 3).

The scheme as constructed required freely supported plate girders spanning the full width of the building to take the load at each floor, as the proposed plate girders without end restraint could no longer carry the entire load.

Proposed scheme employing welded plate girders at second and third floor levels, each restrained at either end and together capable of carrying the entire wall and floor loads from above.

The freeing from end restraint of the two plate girders, which was required by the authority administering the building regulations, resulted in a reduced factor of safety in spite of an increased weight of steel. It should be added, however, in all fairness, that such requirements would not be made under present day regulations.

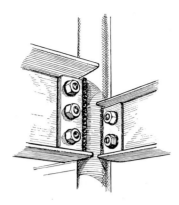

Fig. 4, left, two forms of connection used in the Entertainments Pavilion, Bexhill, England, demonstrate the ease of jointing to circular columns, made possible by welding. (Architects: Eric Mendelsohn and Serge Chermayeff. Engineers: Messrs. Helsby, Hamann and Samuely.)

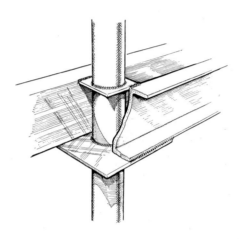

Assembly of steel frame by welding

By means of welding we can now obtain in steel, without the complications of equivalent riveted connections, not only a completely continuous structure such as was formerly associated only with reinforced concrete, but also semi-rigid connections which might be used in seeking economy, to equalise the mid-span and support moments. Fig. 4 shows the ease of jointing to a circular column; a hollow circular section is not only the most efficient compression member but often the most useful architecturally. Welding also provides greater flexibility in the arrangement of the main frame due to the freedom in joint design. Steel saving in welded construction can be around twenty to thirty per cent as compared with a conventional frame, but it should be noted that at the present time, this saving in material may be offset either wholly or in part, by increased costs of fabrication and erection. Whilst the saving in depth and the greatly reduced deflection in continuous beams are particularly useful factors over long spans, rigid joints will result in greater moments being thrown on to the columns, and although these might be designed more economically as hollow sections, it is possible that, at any rate in the U. S. A., fabrication costs would make the use of such columns impractical in multi-storey con-

Fig. 5, Quarry Hill Apartments, Leeds, England. Erection of complete welded eight-storey frame as one unit. (Architect: R. A. H. Livett. Engineers: E. Mopin and Co.)

struction. Research work seems to have indicated that the substitution of a lighter beam due to its continuity may leave the moment transmitted to the column almost unchanged and sometimes even diminished, but in general the beams of a continuous structure will be smaller than those of an equivalent pin-jointed structure, whereas the columns may sometimes be larger. In assembly, welding contributes to the tendency towards the erection of larger pre-assembled units. In several pre-war schemes, complete frames of columns and main beams were erected as single units. One example was a block of five to six storey apartments in France, constructed of pressed steel, in which frames were erected as complete units and spotwelded, the hollow beams and columns being subsequently filled with vibrated concrete to form a composite structure. This was followed by an eight-storey block at Leeds, England, (fig. 5) using rolled steel sections subsequently encased with vibrated concrete.

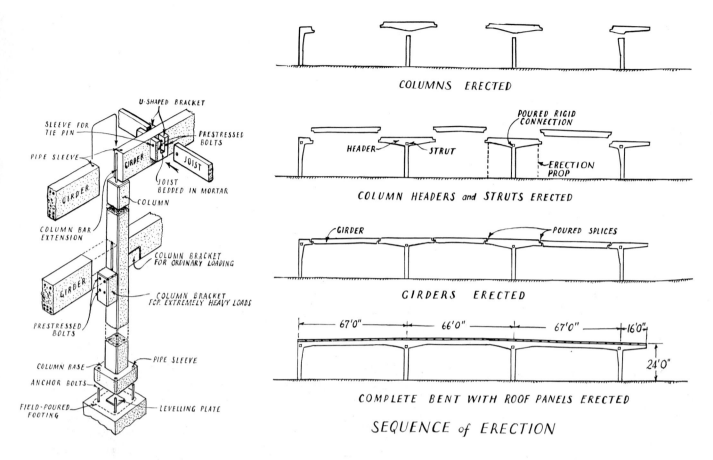

Fig. 6, left above. Method of assembly developed in the U.S.A. for use with standardized pre-cast concrete members, manufactured in lengths up to more than 50 feet. ("Cementstone" system.)

Fig. 7, above and right. Navy Supply Depot, Mechanicsburg, Pennsylvania, constructed of pre-cast units with joints poured in place, demonstrates beam splicing at zones of minimum stress. (Engineer: A. Amirikian.)

The assembly of pre-cast concrete frames

In contrast to this tendency in steel-work, the growing use of pre-cast units in reinforced concrete has resulted in the necessity to sub-divide the structure into components of a kind which can be re-assembled with the minimum field work in such a way as to restore the continuity so inherent in reinforced concrete construction. In low structures where wind pressure is not so important and in cases where spans are not large, a relatively non-rigid joint may be sufficient. Fig. 6 shows a method of assembly developed in the U. S. A. for use with standardized pre-cast concrete members, which is claimed to give good lateral stiffness compared with conventional steel construction. As the detail shows, the principle is that of a "pin-jointed" frame with continuous columns, and with beams supported on pre-cast brackets secured to the columns by means of bolts. This system has been adopted in buildings up to four storeys high with columns erected in complete lengths to a height of more than 50 ft. Brackets may obviously have the same objection for many applications, as haunching in a monolithic frame, and the pre-cast system just described can be used without projecting brackets where lighter loads are involved, as shown in the sketch (fig. 6). Steel connectors can also be used, but this method is more expensive and destroys one of the advantages of the system, namely

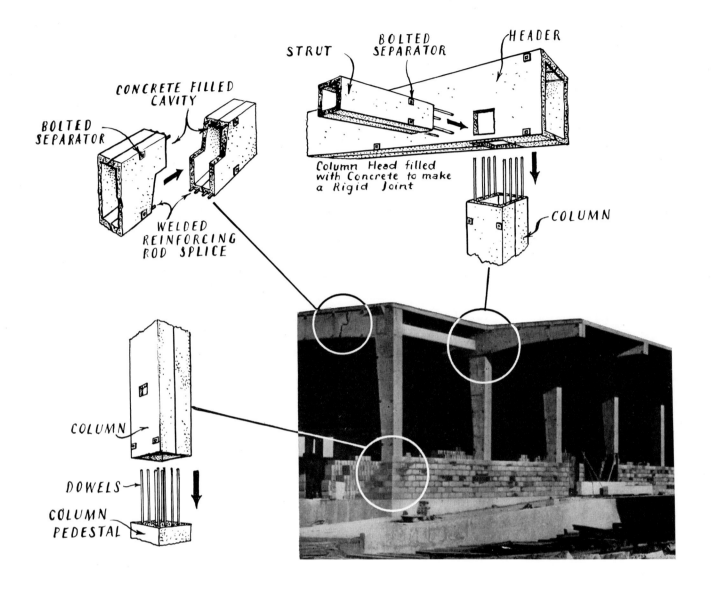

BOLTED SEPARATOR

CONCRETE FILLED CAVITY

WELDED REINFORCING ROD SPLICE

STRUT

BOLTED SEPARATOR

HEADER

Column Head filled with Concrete to make a Rigid Joint

COLUMN

COLUMN

DOWELS

COLUMN PEDESTAL

speed of erection. For multi-storey work, it is more important to retain the continuity of monolithic construction, but the use of field-poured joints to attain this end may destroy the economic advantages of using pre-cast members.

Assembly by means of pre-stressing has been put forward as a possible solution to this problem. The proposal consists of the assembly of complete one-storey frames by the post-tensioning of non-bonded cables threaded through the length of the beams and the tops of the columns. Tests of the monolithic nature of this system seem to have been satisfactory, but it has not yet been applied in practice.

Possibly the biggest field for pre-cast concrete in the future may lie in its use as permanent formwork, particularly when pre-stressed. Joints in such a case provide no problem as they become a part of the field-poured concrete. A variation of this method carried out in the construction of a Navy Storehouse at Mechanicsburg, Pennsylvania, combined a very ingenious system of pre-cast hollow box columns and beams with only the joints poured in place. Fig. 7 shows the sequence of assembly and methods of jointing. Each bent is composed of ten channel-shaped components bolted in pairs, and it is interesting to note that beams are spliced at

Jointing at zones of minimum stress

the zones of minimum stress. This alternative method of obtaining a rigid structure depends upon the ability to produce a rigid bent framing member, either in T or L form. Such members are very easily fabricated in reinforced concrete and a system suitable for multi-storey construction employing this principle is shown in fig. 8. The framing consists of cross-head columns, with beams spanning between the points of minimum stress and connected by means of bolted scarfed joints. Columns are positioned and secured by steel dowels cast into the floor below and grouted through holes in the columns. The example illustrated has load-bearing external walls but the system is equally applicable to a complete skeleton frame. This principle has its application also in welded steel work. Fig. 9 shows the jointing

Fig. 8, warehouse at Clapton, London, employs pre-cast concrete construction with cross-head columns. ('Lambda' system.)

Fig. 9, above, two-hinge welded rigid frames for Dow Chemical Company, Bay City, Michigan, being assembled by site joints at points of minimum stress. (Designers: Austin Company, Engineers and Builders.)

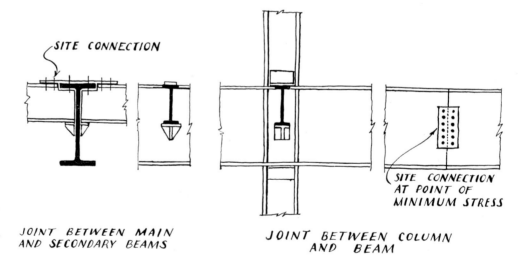

SITE CONNECTION

JOINT BETWEEN MAIN
AND SECONDARY BEAMS

JOINT BETWEEN COLUMN
AND BEAM

SITE CONNECTION
AT POINT OF
MINIMUM STRESS

Fig. 10, right, typical welded joint providing rigid connection between columns and main beams; field connections at points of minimum stress, can be bolted or riveted.

of a two-hinge welded rigid frame at the zones of minimum stress. The welding of erection joints is not always economical so that it is desirable to design the frame for bolted or riveted field connections. In order to retain the advantage of welding at the junction of columns and beams, joints can be arranged as in the reinforced concrete structure, at the points of least moment. Fig. 10 shows such a joint, designed to obtain the maximum benefit from the use of welding.

Fig. 11, above, steel girders are continuous through main trusses and have one connection in each bay at the assembly works of General Motors Corporation, Wilmington, Delaware. (Architect and Engineer: Albert Kahn, Associated Architects and Engineers, Inc.)

Beams continuous over several spans can often be arranged to take advantage of this method of jointing. In the case of multi-storey buildings, it has been done by using two channels, one either side of the column instead of the usual I-beam. This has the added advantage of providing an unrestricted vertical duct down the whole length of the column. Or in the case of built-up welded columns as used in the Leeds apartment buildings (fig. 5), I-beams can be carried through them. Fig. 11 shows a plant at Wilmington, Delaware, where steel girders are continuous through main trusses, being supported on special seatings. Each girder projects about 6 ft. at one end, and is connected at the other end to the cantilevered end of a similarly supported adjacent girder. By this means a saving in weight up to twenty-seven per cent was possible, compared with a simply supported span. This system is very sensitive, however, as any defect in a single joint influences the stability of the whole structure. An alternative and more stable method is the use of two joints in

Fig. 12, three photographs showing the 300 ft. span steel trusses carried over three parallel bays at the Boeing Aircraft Plant II, Renton, Washington.

every second span (see fig. 36). This system was used in an extension to the Boeing Aircraft Plant at Renton (fig. 12) where steel trusses span three bays, each of 300 ft. span. The footings for the columns had to be carried on piles, and it was, therefore, not deemed advisable to make the structure completely rigid. By cantilevering the two end trusses into the centre span and supporting on these cantilevers a 172 ft. freely suspended truss, two joints were made, to allow for movement without losing the advantages of continuity. The same arrangement can be seen in the purlins of the steel plant shown in fig. 36, but in this case, instead of a direct connection at the joints, the free span has been suspended from the cantilevered span to form a series of high-low bays for lighting purposes.

Multi-Storey Framing

In multi-storey structures, the usual requirement of horizontal and vertical surfaces normally necessitates the use of column and beam as distinctive units, even if they are continuous in character. There is no reason, however, why rigid frames cannot be used in multi-storey construction, and an example of superimposed rigid steel frames is shown in fig. 13, where, in a weaving mill in Germany the internal shape was evidently acceptable. The arrangement of the splay on the exterior providing a vertical surface internally, has been carried out in single-storey construction both in timber and in reinforced concrete, and this treatment in multi-storey construction might perhaps provide an interesting solution.

Superimposed rigid frames

Fig. 15, left, Vierendeel truss of about 59 ft. span used at the Headquarters of the Royal Institute of British Architects, Portland Place, London. (Architect: G. Grey Wornum. Engineers: R. T. James & Partners.)

Fig. 14, right, typical Vierendeel truss in welded steel.

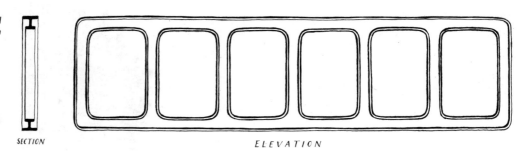

SECTION   ELEVATION

Use of large rigid units

    The use of larger rigid units in cage form is probably of greater value in multi-storey structures than the simple rigid frame. The Vierendeel truss form (fig. 14) permits the use of one or more storey heights to accommodate its depth over large spans without interfering with internal communication or external openings, as would be done by the triangulation of an equivalent lattice girder. It is generally heavier than an equivalent lattice girder of the same depth and loading, but is simpler to fabricate and erect. Welding is especially useful for this construction as large moments are concentrated at the junctions of vertical and horizontal members. Riveting can be used, however, as in the truss at the London Headquarters of the Royal Institute of British Architects (fig. 15). In this case it was necessary to transfer the load of an office floor and a flat roof to external columns in order to keep the load clear of a compound beam at a lower level. The span is about 59 ft. and the truss which is over 10 ft. deep, carries the office floor at the level of the lower chord and a flat roof at the level of the upper chord, allowing window openings in every panel. Reinforced concrete lends itself particularly to this type of structural unit, as illustrated in fig. 16, which shows a part of the Bank of the Nation Building,

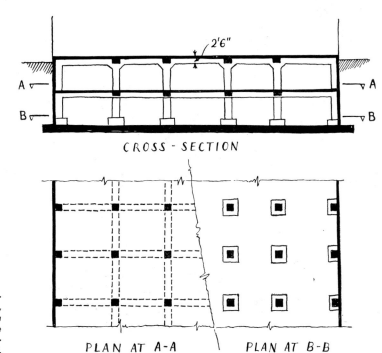

2'6"

CROSS - SECTION

PLAN AT A-A   PLAN AT B-B

Fig. 18, foundation of the Albany Telephone Building, New York, designed as a rigid Vierendeel type frame about 24 ft. deep to counteract effects of shrinkable clay.

Fig. 16, far left, four-storey reinforced concrete Vierendeel truss of about 83 ft. span forms the external wall of the Bank of the Nation Building, Buenos Aires.

Fig. 17, near left, circular footings of mass concrete with no reinforcement, disperse onto a gravel bottom a load of 1600 tons from a 24 storey building in Brazil.

Buenos Aires, in which a four-storey Vierendeel truss spans about 83 ft. The concentration of loads resulting from such large spans in multi-storey construction is demonstrated in the case of the double column in the centre of the illustration, which transmits a load of 6,600 tons. It is interesting to note that owing to the high cost of steel in South America, large circular concrete footings are normally used without reinforcing steel; fig. 17 shows one such footing resting on gravel which carries a load of 1,600 tons from a twenty-four storey building. Foundations provide a more unusual application of the Vierendeel principle in the case of the Albany Telephone Building (fig. 18), where there are three basements in reinforced concrete and eleven storeys of super-structure in steel framing. The building had to be erected on a soft shrinkable clay of low bearing capacity, and a raft type of foundation was therefore decided upon to give a minimum general settlement and one which would be as uniform as possible. The two basements and raft were, therefore, combined into a rigid structure about 24 ft. deep which has been found to function quite satisfactorily. It seems possible that this system might be equally useful where site conditions necessitate the combining of groups of column foundations.

Height and the choice of framing material

In addition to the general arrangement of framing members and the use of larger units of mutually supporting members to increase the flexibility of the multi-storey skeleton frame, the choice and application of structural materials has an important bearing on the architectural development of multi-storey construction. In skyscraper construction column sizes are clearly a decisive factor demanding the use of steel where this is freely and cheaply available. Considering buildings of average height, however, both for the U. S. A. and elsewhere, dead weight may exert a more important influence than that of bulk in the selection of a structural material, although there are also many other factors to be considered. On the one hand, steel has been found economical in high office buildings, hotels, etc. where loading is light compared with an equivalent reinforced concrete structure whose dead weight would be disproportionate to the loads carried. Conversely, reinforced concrete is considered to be well suited for supporting vibrating machinery or heavy floor loading of the warehouse type. In skyscraper construction, steel has been considered a necessity above a certain height, due to the bulk of the columns, and the highest pure reinforced concrete building, until a few years ago, was one of twenty storeys in New York City. Beyond this height it was considered necessary to introduce steel sections into the lower storey columns to form composite members, and in this way a thirty-two storey building was erected in Chicago. This situation, however, was due partly to the regulations governing reinforced concrete construction, which even to-day differ very considerably from one country to another. To give only one comparison, a column with helical binding, under U. S. regulations, requires eighty per cent more volume than one designed under the Brazilian code.[1] In general, the regulations in Brazil are of such a nature as to allow more flexibility in design; added to this are the high cost of steel and comparatively cheap labour, the result being that tall reinforced concrete buildings abound in South American cities.[2] The latest examples are a forty storey building in Sao Paulo and a fifty storey hotel in Rio de Janeiro. On the other hand, the New York Housing Authority in a recent scheme, employed blocks of not more than thirteen storeys although using controlled concrete. It was considered that fourteen storeys was the economic limit of a reinforced concrete framed building, due to the working limit at which concrete can be efficiently placed by crane and bucket. This may, however, only be the outcome of high labour costs in the U. S. A. The economical height of buildings in steel or reinforced concrete seems, therefore, to be connected very much with local conditions, such as the material-labour cost factor and the ability to make full use of technical progress. It is dependent, however, on more than the structural technique and suitable material, as discussed in the next chapter, so that the eighty-five storey Empire State Building may yet remain for all time the highest building to be erected.

[1] The latest regulations in England are inclined to be closer to the Brazilian than the U.S. code.

[2] See Arthur J. Boase "South American Building is Challenging" in Engineering News-Record, 19th October, 1944.

Fig. 19, three-hinged lattice steel arches of 377 ft. span in the Galerie des Machines, International Exhibition, Paris, 1889. (Engineer: Cottancin. Architect: Dutert.)

Single-Storey Framing

Recent years have seen the greatest advances in the spanning of space in single-storey structures, not so much in the extent of the spans, as in the ease of construction and the new methods and materials employed. In the Galerie des Machines at the 1889 Paris Exhibition (fig. 19) a span of 377 ft. was achieved at a time when construction in iron was barely a century old; since that time, however, spans of this magnitude in building seem rarely to have been in demand, and it is only with the rapid development of the airplane that we are faced today with increasing demands for spans of this order. Nevertheless, the addition of timber and reinforced concrete to the solution of such roofing problems, in which shape is governed only by the shedding of rainwater and provision of lighting, has greatly increased the range of possible forms.

Nature of developments

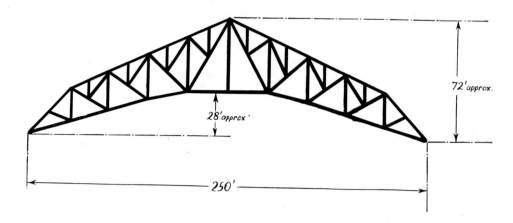

72' approx.

28' approx.

250'

MAIN TRUSS

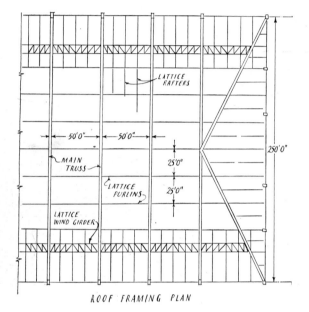

LATTICE RAFTERS

50'0"

50'0"

250'0"

MAIN TRUSS

25'0"

LATTICE PURLINS

25'0"

LATTICE WIND GIRDER

ROOF FRAMING PLAN

Fig. 20, left and above, triangulated steel trusses of 250 ft. span placed at 50 ft. centres are used at the Earls Court Exhibition building, London. (Architect and Engineer: C. Howard Crane.)

Beam and column forms in steel

Beam and column construction in single-storey buildings is normally associated with steel since the dead weight of reinforced concrete limits its application in beam form. Triangulated steel trusses are normally acceptable since the structural depth must be in the roof itself, and the problem is mainly one of keeping it to a minimum by the interpenetration of framing members. The additional cost of increasing the span for buildings of considerable area seems not to be as great as is sometimes supposed, so long as truss spacing is increased appropriately with truss spans. This is particularly noticeable in spans up to about 100 ft. where the spacing would be about 20 ft., and increasing this gradually to 50 ft. with an increase of span up to 250 ft., is said to show a definite economy.[3] Trusses of this span were used at Earls Court Exhibition, London, (fig. 20) arranged in this way and with a series of trussed purlins at 25 ft. centres. This triangular type of truss is more usually employed in combination with parallel chord trusses to take the main span, as seen in fig. 21 where the latter are incorporated under the apex of the secondary trusses. In constructing aircraft factories in the U. S. A. during the war, 300 ft. spans were covered with parallel chord trusses, as for instance in the Boeing Aircraft Plant (fig. 12). In saw-tooth roofs, the main trusses usually run behind the glazing, and this is clearly a neater solution. Better still, the replacement of secondary trusses

[3]See S. McConnel—'Economics of Steel Roofing' in Civil Engineering (England)—May, 1945.

Fig. 21, left, inter-penetration of main parallel chord and secondary triangular trusses in a garage at Inkerman Barracks, Woking, England.

Fig. 22, right, lattice girders in the roof planes with common compression chord, span 60 ft. between rigid frames in this factory for British Celanese Ltd., Wigan, England. (Engineers: Sir Alexander Gibb and Partners.)

by rigid frames as seen in the factory at Wigan, England (fig. 22) provides an internal space which is uninterrupted by structural members. Although the south slope of this roof is comparatively flat, it is actually designed as a lattice girder with I-sections as compression members and rods as tension members, so that the roof consists of a lattice girder in each roof slope having common compression chords at the ridge and spanning 60 ft. between rigid frames. An interesting application of this system on a much larger scale is to be found in an all-welded factory at Waltham Cross, England. As shown in fig. 23, the rigid frames of the previous example are replaced by 500 ft. long lattice girders with only two intermediate supports designed to provide the minimum internal obstruction. These girders are themselves particularly noteworthy for the humps which have been provided over the intermediate columns, in order to cater economically for the large negative moments occurring at these points. The web system of these girders follows the profile of the saw-tooth roof whose inclined rigidly interconnected trusses span 125 ft. between corresponding web members. This arrangement gives an assembly with very clean lines, permitting the roof covering and valley gutters to have an unobstructed passage through the main girders, as can be seen from the aerial view of the factory. The rigid nature of this saw-tooth roof makes it similar in conception to the folded types of roof referred to later (see page 94).

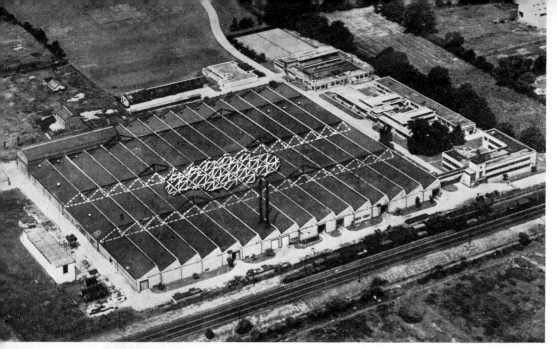

Fig. 23, all-welded roof of the factory for Murex Welding Processes, Ltd., Waltham Cross, England, has 500 ft. long main girders continuous over four supports, carrying inclined saw-tooth girders of 125 ft. span rigidly inter-connected in the roof planes. (Architect: A. Llewelyn Roberts. Engineer: E. S. Needham.)

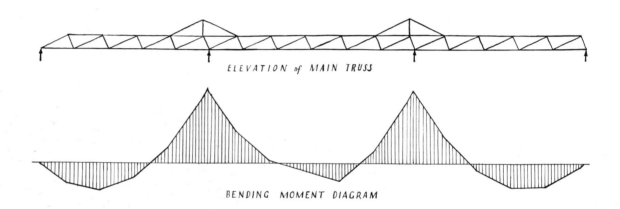

ELEVATION of MAIN TRUSS

BENDING MOMENT DIAGRAM

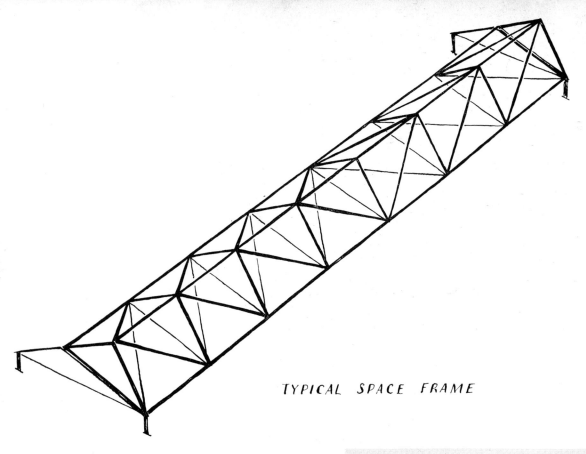

TYPICAL SPACE FRAME

Fig. 24, right and above, triangulated steel
"space frames" of about 68 ft. span were
erected as complete units in this factory at
Byfleet, Surrey, England. (Architect: H. J.
Spiwak. Engineer: O. Safir.)

The use of the combined action of two lattice girders, one in each roof slope, has been developed into a system designed to overcome the disadvantages of site connections and temporary bracing required in the erection of conventional roof trusses. As shown in fig. 24, suitable horizontal bracing of the inclined lattice girders creates a rigid lattice framework by triangulation in three dimensions. This has been called a "space frame" and shows once again the tendency towards the prefabrication of larger rigid structural units. In a factory at Byfleet, England (fig. 24), with a maximum span of about 68 ft., the whole space frame was assembled on the ground together with spandrel trusses and hoisted as one complete unit on to the columns. Designs based on this system have been prepared for spans up to 120 ft.

The space frame

Fig. 26, left, reinforced concrete roof truss of 85 ft. span in Brazil has exposed steel tension members.

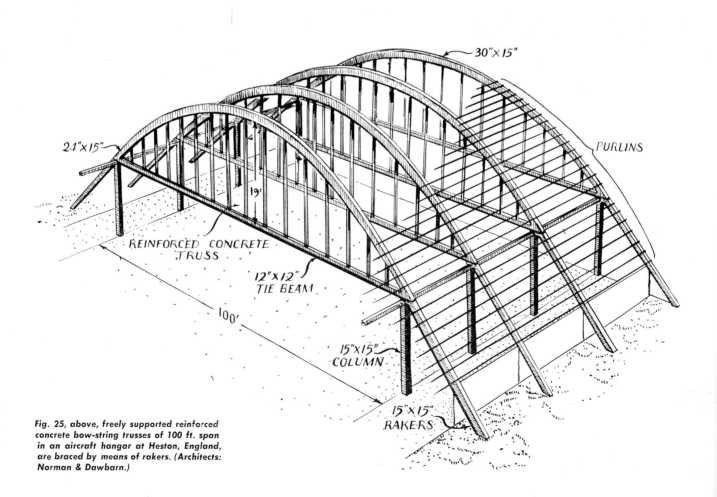

30"x15"

24"x15"

PURLINS

19'

REINFORCED CONCRETE TRUSS

12"x12" TIE BEAM

100'

15"x15" COLUMN

15"x15" RAKERS

Fig. 25, above, freely supported reinforced concrete bow-string trusses of 100 ft. span in an aircraft hangar at Heston, England, are braced by means of rakers. (Architects: Norman & Dawbarn.)

The use of reinforced concrete trusses has so far been very limited mainly owing to the dead weight of the material. An airplane hangar at Heston airport, England, erected in 1929 (fig. 25) has a bow-string truss of 100 ft. span with provision for expansion at the bearings, but it was necessary to provide abutments in the form of rakers, and the structure approaches the complete arch form. This was essentially a pin-jointed structure and not suited to the monolithic nature of reinforced concrete, and we find the later development tending towards the use either of a parabolic arch springing off abutment slabs from below ground level, or of rigid frames with or without ties. One method of reducing weight is shown in fig. 26, which illustrates a truss used in a building in Brazil spanning 85 ft., where tension members have been left exposed; this has obvious disadvantages, however, from the point of view of fire and corrosion. A smaller scale example of weight reduction, which is particularly desirable in pre-cast members, is the prototype pre-cast trussed beam (fig. 27), designed for a span of 24 ft. In members of this form, it is quite possible to introduce a degree of reverse loading by a suitable stressing of the tension chord which might counteract the dead load deflection.

Beam and column framing in reinforced concrete

Fig. 28, storey-height reinforced concrete trusses built up of pre-cast units have pre-stressed bottom chords, in the factory for Colodense, Ltd., Bristol, England. (Architect: E. F. Peat. Engineer: F. J. Samuely.)

Applications of pre-stressing

The development of pre-stressing (see Appendix) is probably the most important contribution towards increasing the economic span of reinforced concrete beams. Lattice girders with post-tensioned ties were used at Berlin-Tempelhof airport, and trusses in reinforced concrete up to 260 ft. span have been constructed by this method.[4] An interesting example is that of a factory at Bristol, England, (fig. 28) where the storey-height trusses designed for very heavy loading are built up out of pre-cast units, comprising two main compression members of arch form, vertical ties of ordinary reinforced concrete and a main tie of pre-stressed concrete. The main span is about 33 ft., and trusses are assembled by means of special connectors which are subsequently encased. Pre-cast pre-stressed trusses up to 100 ft. span were being produced in Germany during the war[5] (fig. 29), but the weight of such

[4]See Dr. K. Hajnal-Konyi "Pre-stressed Reinforced Concrete" in The Architects' Journal (England) 6th May, 1943.
[5]See John Mason "A Report on Structural Engineering in Germany" in The Structural Engineer (England) June, 1946.

Fig. 29, right, pre-cast pre-stressed concrete trusses produced in Germany during the second world war. (Photo: British Crown Copyright Reserved.)

Fig. 30, right, the three main beams of each of four hangars at Melsbroeck, Belgium, having a clear span of 164 ft., are reinforced concrete box girders pre-stressed by 420 wires of about ¼ inch diameter placed inside the hollow of the beam.

members obviously imposes a limitation which may make it necessary to break them down into smaller units, as was done in the factory at Bristol. In the hangar at Karachi airport (see fig. 118) a solid I-section was used, with intermediate stiffeners, for a pre-stressed girder spanning 190 ft. over the door opening. This girder, which is 22 ft. deep, picks up the concrete shells forming the main roof. Another type of pre-stressed beam was used in the hangars at Melsbroeck, Belgium, (fig. 30). The beam here, which has a clear span of 164 ft., is an arched box type concrete girder about 10 ft. deep, pre-stressed by means of 420 wires of ¼ inch diameter which are placed inside the trough, and exert a total force of about 1,450 tons. The beams in these hangars were cast on the ground and were jacked up on to their supporting columns. This design was selected in competition with schemes designed for structural steel and ordinary reinforced concrete, but apart from the cost factor which can rarely provide conclusions of general value in view of the importance of local conditions, it was found that this design required the least height of the three schemes to cover the required span.

Fig. 31, left and below, road bridge at Luzancy, France, of 180 ft. span, constructed of pre-cast concrete units assembled by means of post-tensioned cables. (Engineer: E. Freyssinet.)

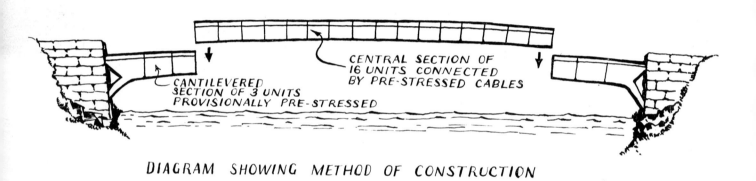

CENTRAL SECTION OF 16 UNITS CONNECTED BY PRE-STRESSED CABLES

CANTILEVERED SECTION OF 3 UNITS PROVISIONALLY PRE-STRESSED

DIAGRAM SHOWING METHOD OF CONSTRUCTION

Fig. 32, above, road bridge at Esbly, France, one of five identical bridges over the River Marne, is a two-hinged shallow arch of pre-stressed concrete construction similar to the Luzancy bridge, but having a span of 240 ft. with a depth of only 3 ft. at mid-span. (Engineer: E. Freyssinet.)

Structural depth was a governing factor in the design of a bridge over the River Marne at Luzancy near Paris (fig. 31) where shipping conditions allowed a depth of only just over 4 ft. for a span of 180 ft. The system adopted was a very flat pre-stressed two-hinged arch which provided the required span/depth ratio of about 45. For various reasons, the pre-stressing was combined with a most unusual method of construction, which might well be applicable to large spans in building work. The bridge consists of three main girders of hollow rectangular section, each composed of twenty two pre-cast units about 8 ft. long. Sixteen of the units of each girder were assembled on the river bank by means of post-tensioned cables to form the central section, which was lowered into position between the two side sections, each composed of three units cantilevered from the abutments by means of pre-stressed cables. Further cables inserted through the length of cantilevers and central portion were subsequently stressed and the compression induced in the girders by the stretching of these tension cables is the only means used to hold the units together. Further bridges have since been constructed on this system over much larger spans and with a much higher span/depth ratio. The remarkable slenderness of these bridges can be seen in the one at Esbly (fig. 32).

Fig. 33, below, parallel chord timber trusses at the Chicago assembly plant of the Douglas Aircraft Co., Inc., have a span of 150 ft. and depth of 18 ft.

Beam and column structures in timber

As in the case of reinforced concrete, the development of timber as an engineering material suitable for long span construction is of comparatively recent origin when we consider the very large spans which were already being carried out in iron a century ago. Particularly great strides were made in the U. S. A. during World War II in an effort to save steel for war purposes. This challenge produced such structures as the Douglas Aircraft Assembly plant at Chicago (fig. 33) where parallel chord timber trusses were used to give a clear span of 150 ft. Constructed with metal shear connectors, these trusses were probably the longest in the U. S. A. when erected, but with a depth of 18 ft. they had a comparatively low span/depth ratio. Fig. 34 shows two types of bow-string truss used in aircraft hangars, with laminated top and bottom chords, and having spans of 160 ft. and

Fig. 34, bow string trusses with glued laminated top and bottom chords; above left, 160 ft. span trusses in a hangar at Tucson, Arizona. (Engineers: Summerbell Roof Structures); above right, 200 ft. span trusses in a hangar at Cleveland, Ohio. (Engineers: Timber Structures, Inc.)

Fig. 35, right, plywood plate girders of 36 ft. span used in the warehouse for the R.C.A. Manufacturing Co. at Camden, New Jersey; probably the first building to use this type of member in the U.S.A.

200 ft. respectively. The web bracings are of different types, and in the shorter span trusses are of a very light character. An even greater span of 223 ft. was attained in a naval hangar at Minneapolis using bow-string trusses with another type of web bracing.

These examples make use of timber in its one-dimensional form, but a signficant development is the plate girder which takes advantage of the new form of timber, i.e., the plywood sheet, in building up the structural member. Timber in this form has the particular advantage of a high strength/weight ratio. What is thought to be the earliest application in the U. S. A. is shown in fig. 35 where a typical girder having double plywood webs with intermediate stiffeners spans 36 ft., but plywood plate girders used later included some with solid plywood webs 1½ inches thick with a span of 60 ft. and a span/depth ratio of 12.

Fig. 36, right and below, rigid main frames in welded steel at the new plant for the Steel Company of Wales at Margam, S. Wales, have rigidly embedded feet, giving lightest possible construction. Cantilevered purlins support lower sections of high-low roof. (Engineers: W. S. Atkins and Partners. Consulting Architects: Sir Percy Thomas and Son.)

Fig. 37, right, double cantilever frames with rigid feet, in welded steel, carry Vierendeel type girders between frames in the main Railway Station at Dusseldorf, Germany.

The methods of single-storey spanning so far considered assume a distinction between the load-collecting beam and its supporting column. The stability of the structure therefore depends either upon the provision of suitable bracing or upon obtaining a degree of rigidity at the joints between beam and column, and/or at the column bases. The extreme cases of the latter conditions are rigidly embedded column feet and two-hinged joints, or hinged column feet and two rigid joints. Most cases of beam and column construction will lie between these limits, having a degree of rigidity both in the column feet and in the joints between beam and column. There is finally the further condition of having all four corners rigid and although this system cannot easily be adopted owing to the difficulty of obtaining complete rigidity at the column bases, it provides the stiffest and lightest possible form of construction. This system has been used in a new steel plant in South Wales (fig. 36) where advantage has been taken of the piles required by site conditions to embed the column feet into the pile caps, creating rigidity at all four corners of the 90 ft. span welded frames. The use of rigid joints both at the foot of the column and at its junction with the cross member, also permits the use of the double cantilever form most commonly encountered in railway platform canopies, such as the one in welded steel at Dusseldorf, Germany, (fig. 37). This form seems to be developing increasing significance in structural design, as will be shown later.

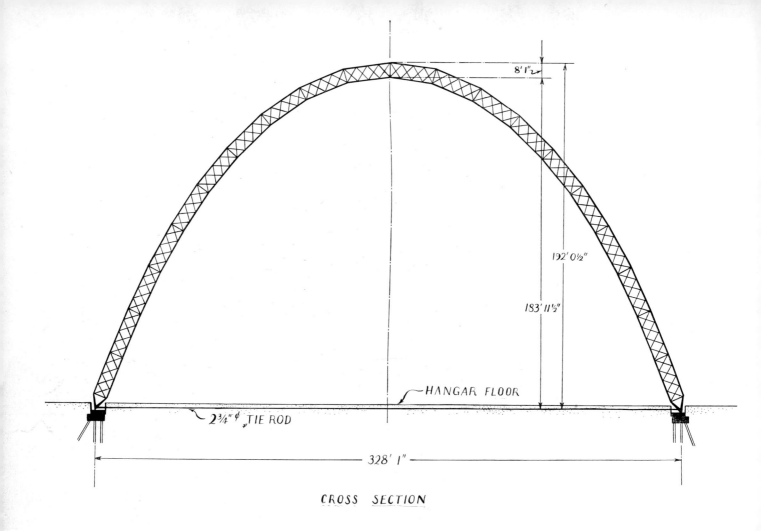

CROSS SECTION

Fig. 38, U. S. Navy blimp hangar with steel
arch ribs of 328 ft. span, tied below floor
level. (Engineer: A. Amirikian.)

The two-hinge
arch and
rigid frame

The complete arch form ranges from the rigid two-pin frame having considerable bending moments to resist, to the parabolic arch rib, which is in almost pure compression. Within this range, as one might expect, the arched or rounded structural form, being less concerned with bending stresses, seems generally to lead to economy of material. For instance, a recent comparison between a 264 ft. span rigid frame and 275 ft. span three-pin arched frame both in steel, is said to have shown that the latter required a considerably smaller quantity of steel than the former.[6] Curved arch forms, however, are normally more applicable to very large spans owing to the inconvenience of their shape, and they usually exert considerable side thrust which requires a tie-rod or adequate abutment. An outstanding example in steel was the U. S. Navy hangar developed to house the coastal patrol blimps during World War II (fig. 38). These hangars had a span of 328 ft. and a rise of 185 ft. and the truss arches, shop welded and field riveted, were supported on pinned shoes connected by tie-rods of 2¾ inch diameter below floor level.

[6]See Fred N. Severud "Hangars Analysed" in Architectural Record, April, 1947.

Fig. 39, passerelle near Menomenee St., Lincoln Park, Chicago, is suspended by means of steel hangers from a welded steel supporting arch. (Engineer: Chief Engineer, Chicago Park District.)

Fig. 40, above, San Francisco-Oakland Bay suspension bridge with a maximum clear span of about 2325 ft. The suspension bridge is the complete expression of the tensile nature of steel. (Photo by Ewing Galloway, N. Y.)

Steel arches

Arches in lattice form, first in cast-iron and later in steel, have been used considerably in large scale construction ever since the introduction of iron as a structural material. Bridge construction has been a particularly fertile field for this form of structure, using the arch either as support for an overhead platform or as a ring from which to suspend the platform at a lower level. With the development of welding, steel has become much more adaptable to the requirements of structural form, so that it becomes possible to mould the solid steel arch to its essential structural shape without the involved processes of riveting. Fig. 39 shows a pedestrian passerelle in Chicago where a steel arch of this kind has been used in its most graceful form, namely as a ring from which to suspend the platform.

The tensile properties of steel have resulted in the development of an entirely new type of arch, an inverted arch of steel cable in pure tension as opposed to the ideal form of normal arch in pure compression. The combination of such cables with vertical suspension members to support the platform, a system familiar in suspension bridges of enormous span (see fig. 40), is perhaps the purest possible expression of the nature of steel.

Fig. 41, rigid steel frames of 200 ft. span
at Long Beach, California, were shop and
field welded and erected as complete units.

Fig. 42, above, riveted steel rigid frames of 222 ft. span at the Oregon State College, Corvallis, Oregon, have tie rods at floor level to take the horizontal thrust. (Architects: G. H. Jones and H. D. Marsh. Engineers: Cooper and Rose.)

Rigid frames in steel

For many applications, even in long span construction, the rigid frame is a more suitable form than the pure arch. Here again, the development of welding, giving **greater powers of control over the structural material, has led to the greater use of** solid rigid frames of considerable span, where lattice construction, and in many cases triangulation, would previously have been used. Fig. 41 shows the 200 ft. span rigid steel frames of a transit shed at Long Beach, California. These frames were shop and field welded and erected as complete units, leaving only 30 per cent of the field welding to be done in the air after erection. In the case of the rather larger span frames of the Basket Ball Coliseum at Oregon State College (fig. 42), riveting was used throughout, but owing to the size limitations imposed by transport facilities, joints had to be located at the knee where stresses are greatest and the resulting joint, as can be seen, was a very complicated one. These frames have a span of 222 ft. with tie rods at floor level to take the horizontal thrust, and their structural form appears to be rather less refined than that of the welded frames seen in fig. 41.

Fig. 43, two-pin 331 ft. span lattice-steel arches of the Aircraft Assembly Hall near Bristol, England, have tie members which materially reduce the stresses in the system. (Engineers: Brian Colquhoun and Partners. Architect: Eric L. G. Ross.)

Fig. 44, above and right, two-hinge rigid frame of lattice construction in welded steel being erected for a hangar in Czechoslovakia.

The concentration of stresses which occur at the knees of these rigid frames can be very high, and in the Aircraft Assembly Hall shown in fig. 43, advantage was taken of the requirement for extensive overhead crane supports to insert high-level ties which materially reduced these stresses. These rigid frames are of riveted lattice construction having a clear span of 331 ft. with the uprights of adjacent frames nested into one another. It is interesting to note that a simple arch type of structure was ruled out in this case owing to the need for a minimum height of 57 ft. over the whole floor area. Lattice construction may well be more suitable in resisting the high stresses involved in the completely rectangular rigid frame such as might be dictated by functional requirements of this kind, but here again welding can provide great improvements in the appearance and form of the structural members. The all welded hangar frame shown in fig. 44 is a particularly interesting example of this kind, although its span is only about a half that of the Aircraft Assembly Hall.

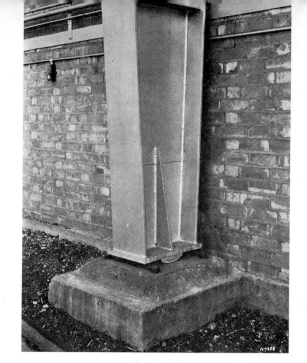

Fig. 45, 80 ft. span two-pin rigid welded steel frames used in a workshop for Messrs. Whessoe at Darlington, England, compared favorably in cost with a conventional triangular truss design. (Engineer: O. Bondy.)

Fig. 47, above, welded steel frames at the Delco plant, Rochester, New York, are shaped to the roof section required for good lighting. (Architect and Engineer: Albert Kahn, Associated Architects and Engineers, Inc.)

Fig. 46, right, rigid welded steel frame of saw-tooth section being erected by welding the rafters to the "tree-form" columns.

Welding has also made the use of rigid frames very suitable for medium span construction and superior in many respects to conventional methods. Fig. 45 shows a welding shop of 80 ft. span which was found to compare favourably in cost with a conventional design of lattice trusses on columns. The functional requirements of light and maintenance were better satisfied and the structure clearly has a greatly improved appearance over the network of truss construction. The advantages of this form of frame can be extended to the saw-tooth roof as shown in fig. 46, and the ability to construct such rigid members makes it possible to shape the members according to the desired roof section, as was done in the plant at Rochester, New York (fig. 47).

Fig. 48, one of the seventeen timber blimp hangars constructed in the United States. With arches spanning 234 ft. in the clear and having an internal height of 157 ft. they are the largest timber structures in the world. Three of them were destroyed in a hurricane. (Engineers: U. S. Bureau of Yards and Docks.)

Fig. 49 A, crescent-type timber trusses of about 140 ft. span with glued laminated chords as used in a number of hangars in the U.S.A., gave high centre clearance for tail-planes. (Engineer: Fred N. Severud.)

Fig. 49 B, crescent-type timber trusses of 160 ft. span in a U. S. Army hangar at Tucson, Arizona.

Timber arches and rigid frames

When steel became a scarce and critical material in the U. S. A. during World War II, blimp hangars similar to those previously erected in steel were constructed in timber (fig. 48), having a clear span of 234 ft. and an internal height of 157 ft. These immense spandrel braced arches, made possible by the use of steel connectors, are thought to be the largest timber structures ever built and were the largest span arches to have been constructed in the U. S. A. Three of these hangars at Richmond, Florida failed and were destroyed in the ensuing fire, when they were hit by a hurricane which reached a velocity of 160 miles an hour, exerting wind forces about two and a half times those for which the structures had been designed. Crescent-type timber trusses were also used in several hangars to provide high clearance at the centre for tail-planes, and the ones shown in fig. 49 have spans of 140 ft. and 160 ft. respectively. Laminated timber, however, lends itself particu-

Fig. 50, glued laminated timber arches of 157 ft. span and 57 ft. rise in the hangars at the Army Modification Center, Vandalia, Ohio, are elliptical in shape and have no tie rods.

Fig. 51, elliptical laminated arches having an equal rise and span of 80 ft. in a research laboratory at Dayton, Ohio. (Engineers: U. S. Army Engineers.)

Fig. 52, segmental laminated timber arches of 120 ft. span used for the Hockey Stadium, Gustaphus Adolphus College, St. Peter, Minnesota, are supported on concrete buttresses. (Engineers: Unit Structures, Inc.)

Fig. 53, above, rigid frames in lattice timber construction give a clear span of 87.5 ft. in this storage building at Shoreham-by-Sea, England. (Engineer: Phillip O. Reece.)

larly to curved forms, and laminated arches have been used for spans up to 175 ft. Elliptical arch ribs of solid glued laminated timber having a span of 157 ft. and a rise of 57 ft. were used in the construction of an aircraft hangar at Vandalia, Ohio (fig. 50). These were erected in three sections, spliced with steel plates and were supported on concrete abutments. Similar arches, but supported on the short axis of the ellipse, were used in a research laboratory at Dayton, Ohio, having an equal span and rise of 80 ft. (fig. 51). Segmental arches are more usual in laminated timber, however, such as those of 120 ft. span over a Hockey Stadium (fig. 52) which are supported on concrete buttresses. Rigid frames in timber seem to have been less common but this form was recently used in a storage building in England (fig. 53) where the frames are of lattice construction, having a span of about 88 ft.

Fig. 55, above, U. S. Navy hangar at San Diego constructed of reinforced concrete, has two-hinged arch ribs of 294 ft. span and 81 ft. rise carrying thin concrete shells at the intrados, presenting a smooth unobstructed surface internally. (Engineers: Roberts and Schaefer Co.)

Fig. 54, above, parabolic concrete arches support the superstructure in the Public Baths at Northampton, England. (Architects: J. C. Prestwich and Sons.)

Fig. 57, above and above right, two road bridges in Sweden of similar design, display the spirit of the new aesthetic in combining the concrete compression arch with slender steel suspension members to support the platform. (a) Bridge over the River Angermanalv at Hammar having four spans of 262 ft. each. (b) Bridge over the River Ume Alv at Ottentrask having two spans of 177 ft. each. (Design System: Christiani and Nielsen, Ltd.)

Fig. 58, right, the 867 ft. span hingeless arch of the bridge over the river Angerman at Sando, Sweden, is the longest existing concrete arch in the world. (Engineers: A. B. Skanska Cementgjuteriet.)

Fig. 56, above, the concrete arch as a bearing ring spanning 197 ft. in the viaduct over the river Rhone at Longeray, France.

Reinforced concrete is particularly suitable for arch rib construction, especially in parabolic form, where the bending stresses are at a minimum and there is thus a great economy in steel. An example of this form is shown in fig. 54. Use of the concrete arch as a stiffening or intermediate rib in shell construction, seems likely to be one of the most fertile fields in the future. The two-hinged arch ribs of the naval hangar at San Diego (fig. 55), having a span of 294 ft., were placed externally, with the shell carried at the intrados providing a smooth internal surface which permitted the use of simple movable formwork. Arches of larger span have since been used for this type of construction (see later fig. 121). The concrete arch has probably been most used in bridge construction, and as in the case of steel, either as a supporting ring (fig. 56) or as a suspension ring in conjunction with steel tension members (fig. 57), but the latter form may well have its applications in building as the demand grows for increased spans in aircraft hangars. The 867 ft. span box-type arch of the bridge over the River Angerman at Sandö, Sweden (fig. 58) is at present the longest span concrete arch in existence. The formwork for constructions of this kind presents a major engineering problem in itself. In this particular instance, the formwork was originally constructed as a framed timber arch across the full span of the river owing to the poor nature of the soil below the deep river bed. The whole of the bottom slab of the arch had already been concreted when this formwork suddenly collapsed into the river, mainly as a result of excessive moisture in the timber. Eventually the formwork was supported on piles driven into the river bed. The French engineer, Freyssinet, apparently considers it possible to construct a reinforced concrete arch of 3,270 ft. span costing only a half that of an equivalent suspension bridge, but he limits the maximum possible span to 6,000 ft. for practical and economic reasons connected with the formwork.

Fig. 59, above, flight hangar for Curtiss-Wright Company, Buffalo, New York, has seven continuous spans, each of 130 ft. in reinforced concrete. (Architects: Duane Lyman and Associates. Engineers: T. H. McKaig, J. F. McGill and Prof. C. E. O'Rourke.)

Reinforced concrete rigid frames

In rigid frames the large moments at the knee normally produce an uneconomical weight of material for large spans in reinforced concrete, unless adjacent spans permit a continuous structure, as in the hangar at Buffalo (fig. 59) which has seven continuous spans of 130 ft. each. A solution to this is to be found in the use of a hollow box section such as that employed in a hangar at Des Moines, Iowa (fig. 60). These 140 ft. span rigid reinforced concrete frames, comparatively flat in shape and tapered towards the feet, are 7 ft. wide and have a wall thickness varying from 7 to 10 inches. This principle of the hollow section approaches the conception of the airship hangars at Orly referred to later (fig. 135).

Three-hinge arches and frames

It may be convenient for erection purposes, or for other reasons, to have a three-pin frame which can be erected in two halves and which at the same time becomes statically determinate, as opposed to the two-pin arch and rigid frame which are indeterminate structures and more sensitive to effects of foundation settlement or temperature change. The normal design of rigid frames entails an assumption sufficiently accurate for small spans as to the probable position of the hinges or points of minimum bending, but for large spans it is thought advisable to form the hinges in order to obtain greater accuracy and consequent economy. Certain German engineers go so far as to say that if a pin is assumed in the stress analysis, it should be used on the job, otherwise the conditions of the design are vitiated. The shape of the rigid frame enables horizontal thrust to be overcome more easily than with an arch rib, and this was one of the achievements of the three-hinge frames in the Galerie des Machines[7] (fig. 19) which was constructed without tie-rods. Height in relation to span is an important factor, however, in the economy of a three-pin frame, and where this is restricted it may be necessary to use tie-rods to reduce the bending moment at the knee or to reduce the horizontal thrust, especially where poor soil conditions are encountered. If this is done, the three-hinge principle is forsaken and the advantages of accurate statical calculations and freedom from stresses due to settlement or temperature change, are lost. In fact, it is probable that where sufficient height is not available, the use of a two-hinge frame would be more economical.

[7]See Sigfried Giedion "Space, Time and Architecture" page 204. (Harvard University Press).

Fig. 61, below, three-hinged arch ribs in riveted steel in the hangars at Idlewild Airport, New York, spring from buttresses and have a clear span of 300 ft. (Engineers: Roberts and Schaefer Co.)

Fig. 62, above, three-hinged steel frames of lattice construction, spanning 275 ft. between pins, were used in two airplane hangars at Chanute Field, Rantoul, Illinois.

Where spans become very large, it may not be economical to provide a correspondingly great height, and it seems that with the increasingly large spans being called for in airplane hangars, there is a tendency towards the use of the true arch form, either tied or buttressed, whether in steel or in reinforced concrete. The new hangars at Idlewild Airport, New York (fig. 61) are constructed of three-hinged parabolic arch ribs, shop and field riveted, with a constant depth of 4½ ft. across the solid webs. These ribs have a clear span of 300 ft. and spring from large concrete buttresses which are themselves flanked by ancillary buildings. It is interesting to note that although this scheme produced a lower bid than a design for a concrete shell of 6 inch average thickness supported on arch ribs (the type shown in figs. 55 and 121), comparative analyses of the costs of different roof types in steel and concrete, resulted in the adoption of shell construction for the 257 ft. span hangars of American Airlines at Chicago. Departure from the true arch form is seen in the three hinged lattice steel frames of two hangars constructed at Rantoul, Illinois (fig. 62). These frames span 275 ft. between hinge centres and derive their shape from bending down, as it were, the true arch of the upper part, into vertical supporting legs thereby obtaining the height required for reduction of horizontal thrust and for the functional requirements of the hangar.

Fig. 63, left, demountable type of hangar used in Germany during second world war, employed three-hinge arches erected by drawing the two springing pins together. (Photo: British Crown Copyright Reserved.)

An interesting way of making use of the hinged arch was developed in Germany during the war in the form of demountable hangars, one of which is shown in fig. 63. The whole hangar is assembled, complete with roof covering, flat on the ground, and is then raised into position by drawing the two springing pins together and tying them. The two halves of the hangar revolve about the centre pin as they rise into the air, the springings revolving on bearers as they are drawn in.

For smaller spans the rigid frame form is usually more suitable than the arch owing to height requirements. The architectural advantage to be gained from this form, permitting expressive use of material as opposed to the maze of truss and column construction, is clearly shown in a garage in Holland (fig. 64) having solid web three-hinge frames of about 80 ft. span. This example is of riveted construction; the difficulty of fabricating such frames undoubtedly restricted the development of this form for small and medium span construction, but the use of welding may well encourage their employment in the future. Shortage of steel during the war encouraged a parallel development of three-hinge frame construction in timber and reinforced concrete, both of which can be employed economically to produce forms which follow stress distribution.

Fig. 64, above and below, refined type of three-hinged frame in riveted steel used in a garage at The Hague, Holland, has a span of about 80 ft.

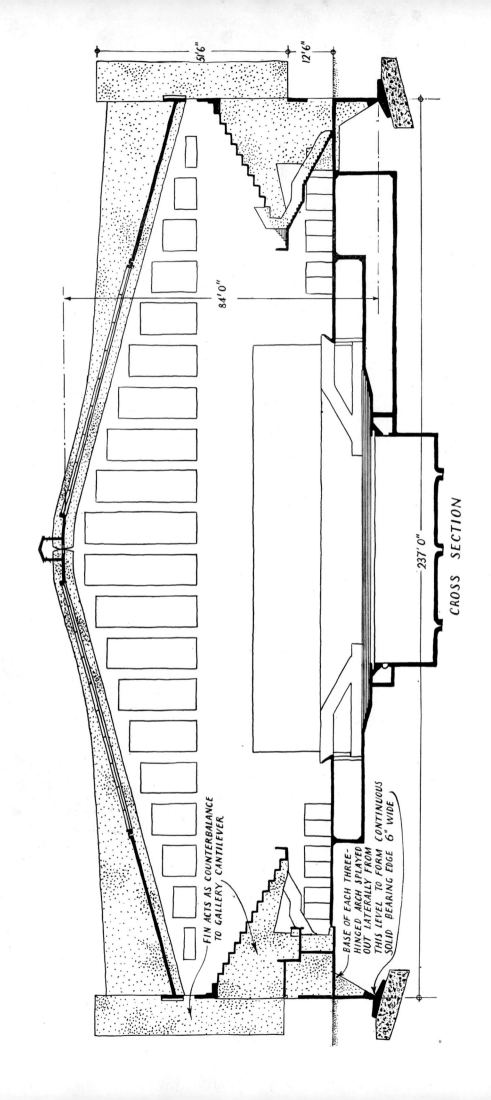

CROSS SECTION

51'6" 12'6"

84'0"

237'0"

FIN ACTS AS COUNTERBALANCE
TO GALLERY CANTILEVER

BASE OF EACH THREE-
HINGED ARCH SPLAYED
OUT LATERALLY FROM
THIS LEVEL TO FORM CONTINUOUS
SOLID BEARING EDGE 6" WIDE

Fig. 65, left and above, the Empire Pool at Wembley, England, was constructed with 237 ft. span three-hinged arches in reinforced concrete. Their shape is governed by the counter-balance of external fins and internal gallery. Loads are spread along a continuous bearing edge 6 inches wide. (Architect and Engineer: Sir E. Owen Williams.)

In England, reinforced concrete was the alternative material to steel. It had been used to construct the 237 ft. span three-hinged arches at the Empire Pool in London (fig. 65), but the wartime need of constructing large numbers of medium span structures at great speed could not be met by concrete poured in place. Earlier development in pre-casting had in general followed the forms of steel but the three-hinge frame, more suited to the material and providing greater stability, was the form developed and extensively used in the building programme during World War II. (Similar designs were prepared for use in the tropics with adobe reinforced with bamboo). Fig. 66 shows the erection of one of these frames; although they are considered practical up to a span of 150 ft., the most economical span for a given area is thought to be about 60 ft. Up to 40 ft. span they can be prefabricated and transported to the site but above this it is most economical to cast them on the site in a convenient position for erection. Cantilevered frames such as that shown in fig. 67 can be useful in certain cases, and may even be instrumental in economising in steel, as was the case in the building illustrated, since the moment at the knee becomes counterbalanced.

Three-hinge construction in reinforced concrete

Fig. 66, above, erection of typical three-hinged pre-cast concrete frame, after casting on the site. (Engineers: C. W. Glover and Partners.)

TYPICAL
TREE-FORM
MEMBER

Fig. 67, right and below, introduction of a cantilever into the frame reduces the stresses by counterbalancing the bending moment at the knee.

Fig. 68, right, mushroom-headed columns in the Administration Building, Johnson Wax Company, at Racine, Wisconsin, are virtually hinged at the feet. Stability is provided by means of mutual support. (Architect: Frank Lloyd Wright.)

As an extension to this principle and in contrast to the self-supporting double cantilever with rigid foot, a series of double cantilevers could be used with little or no rigidity at the feet if they were arranged to give each other mutual support, on the principle of the three-hinged frame, and quite a variety of forms could be devised by appropriate shaping of the cantilever arms according to the desired roof profile. The Johnson Administration Building in Racine (fig. 68) illustrates this principle, the slender column feet being virtually hinged, and stability being provided by the mutual support of the mushroom heads, rigidly connected to the tapered supporting shafts.

Fig. 69, above and below, three-hinged laminated timber frames of I section were used in this 120 ft. span industrial plant in the U.S.A. (Architects and Engineers: H. L. Gogerty. Consulting Engineer, S. B. Barnes.)

Fig. 70, below, glued laminated arches of 52 ft. span in the Recreation Building, U.S. Naval Training Station, Great Lakes, Illinois, have the clean lines of a rectangular section. (Architects: Skidmore, Owings and Merrill. Engineers: Unit Structures, Inc.)

Timber forms of three-hinged frames

In the U. S. A., timber became the substitute for steel and the three-pin frame has been used on a large scale in laminated timber, although actual pin joints are not normally used. One industrial plant, for instance, was constructed with I-section three-hinged frames in laminated timber over a span of 120 ft. (fig. 69). These had a rise of 72 ft. with a maximum depth at the knee of 4 ft. A rectangular section, however, may be easier to fabricate, as was apparently found in Germany, and its use seems more desirable in most cases where the frame is to be exposed, as in the Recreation Building at Great Lakes, Illinois (fig. 70) which is typical of many medium span applications. Spans up to 100 ft. are quite usual in this form. A more unusual application of timber to the alleviation of wartime steel shortage is to be seen in the all timber aircraft plant at Hammondsport, New York

Fig. 71, right and below, three-hinged laminated timber arches of lattice type, spanning 60 ft. with 17 ft. cantilever arms at either side, formed the main framing in the all-timber plant for Mercury Aircraft, Inc. at Hammondsport, New York. (Architect: Ervay J. Baker.)

(fig. 71). The three-pin cantilevered arches, which were designed to have a minimum of tension members and at the same time to use the least possible amount of timber, have a span of 60 ft. and a clearance of 20 ft. down the centre aisle; subassembly mezzanines required along either side, were provided by means of 17 ft. cantilever arms from which they were suspended. The main arches are of laminated timber with glued joints, connected laterally by timber purlin trusses. The whole system which included prefabricated plywood panels for walls, floors and roofs, was apparently found to be moderate in price and easy to erect. An interesting point about these frames is that they combine the free curves of reinforced concrete with the lattice construction of steel by exploiting the new timber techniques, to produce an expressive form peculiar to the material.

Fig. 72, above, Lamella type roof in steel at the Horseley Piggott Works, Tipton, England. It consists of short lengths of pressed steel bar, freely connected in a diagonal grid, the whole system being arched by means of ties which take the horizontal thrust.

Fig. 73, right, Lamella roof in timber over a Sports Arena at Eugene, Oregon, has the uniform arch thrust distributed onto buttresses. (Architects: Laurence and Holford, Engineers: Blood and Williams.)

"Lamella" type of continuous arch

The forms of arch construction so far considered have been those derived from a framework of parallel arch ribs placed at varying intervals, which have to be bridged by purlins or other suitable forms of infilling. The arch, however, also lends itself to the use of a series of small framing members arranged on a diagonal grid and producing a continuous arch or barrel vault based on the principle of mutually supporting members, referred to later in rigid construction. In the system to be considered first the elements are not rigidly connected, and they can therefore only be used in arched form, when suitably tied or buttressed, or when having sufficient rise to enable horizontal thrust to be taken in the foundations. These "lamella" type structures, as they are called, have been carried out in all the three principal structural materials. Fig. 72 shows an example in England constructed of short lengths of pressed steel suitably stiffened at the ends and edges, and bolted together at their intersections. The shape of the arched roof is maintained by the combined action of transverse tie rods and longitudinal pressed steel purlins, which can be seen in the illustration. This arch has continuous support along its edges, as has

Fig. 74, above, left and right, a hangar near Rome having a roof of Lamella type in reinforced concrete, buttressed at regular intervals on three sides, with the thrust on the opening side carried to three massive buttresses by means of a space frame. (Engineer: Pier Luigi Nervi.)

Fig. 75, below, left and right, a second hangar near Rome of modified design has the Lamella type roof composed of pre-cast reinforced concrete lattice members with only six supporting buttresses. (Engineer: Pier Luigi Nervi.)

also the timber roof of the same type at Eugene, Oregon (fig. 73). The latter, however, comes down on to a series of buttresses which eliminates the necessity for transverse tie rods. The use of buttress supports was developed in a very remarkable manner in two reinforced concrete hangars near Rome, the first of which was constructed during World War II, and both of which are designed on the lamella principle. The first hangar (fig. 74) which was poured in sections with the use of standard formwork, is 147 ft. wide and 366 ft. long; the roof is carried on three sides by means of regularly spaced buttresses, but on the entrance side there are only three buttresses which pick up the load from the arched roof by means of a space frame spanning between them. The second hangar (fig. 75) is constructed out of pre-cast units which are of lattice type, except in the region of the supports, and which are assembled by means of a special four-way connecting unit. The dimensions of this hangar are 120 ft. by 366 ft. and the whole roof is carried on only six supporting buttresses.

Fig. 76, above, the parabolic arched roof of rigid diagonal framing in welded steel over a 56 ft. wide Badminton Hall at Epsom, England, maintains its own arched shape and therefore requires no ties or buttresses. (Architect: W. Wiltshire. Engineers: Diagrid Structures, Ltd.)

Rigid type of continuous arch

The lamella type structures just described are dependent on the provision of resistance to horizontal thrust both laterally and longitudinally. If the members are rigidly connected in the roof plane, however, ties and buttresses can be eliminated since the structure maintains its own shape and there is no lateral thrust to be resisted. This system, carried out in welded steel, is seen in the roof of a Badminton Hall at Epsom, England (fig. 76), which has a span of 56 feet. The arched roof is composed of a series of folds approximating in shape to a parabola and built up out of 8 inch deep steel joists arranged in a diagonal grid. Although larger spans could be attained in this way, the required rise might be rather excessive as spans increased, in order to keep down the bending stresses due to the tendency of the arch to spread at its base. In fact, where the shape of the structure is such as to give rise to considerable lateral thrust and buttresses or ties are undesirable, the most efficient way of resisting the thrust is to make the structure itself a rotational one, in which spreading can be resisted by means of a tension ring.

Fig. 78, above and right, lattice-type dome in tubular chrome-nickel steel, encloses the 100 ft. diameter aviary for high-flying birds at the Zoological Gardens, Rome.

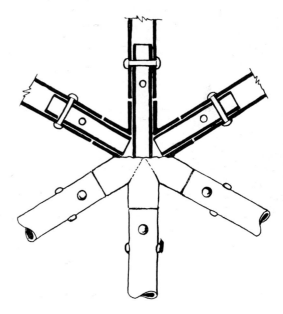

TYPICAL JOINT DETAIL

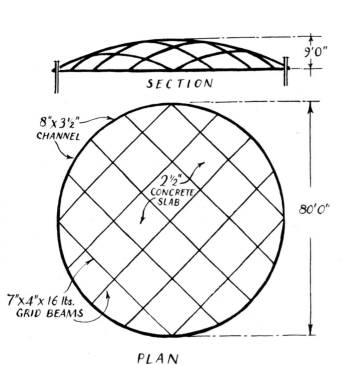

9'0"

SECTION

8"x 3½" CHANNEL

2½" CONCRETE SLAB

80'0"

7"x 4"x 16 lbs. GRID BEAMS

PLAN

Fig. 77, left, typical design for a saucer dome of 80 ft. diameter, in rigid steel diagonal grid framing. (Engineers: Diagrid Structures, Ltd.)

Rotational structures

The dome is the most common form of this type of structure, and if constructed of skeleton framing, the latter must have sufficient rigidity to maintain the shape of the dome in order to act as the rotational version of the arch rib. The flatter the dome, however, the higher will be the stresses in the joints between framing members, so that if a flat dome is required to be built up of small framing members on the principle of the previous examples, it could be suitably carried out in welded steel or reinforced concrete. Fig. 77 shows a typical scheme for a saucer dome in welded steel having a diameter of 80 feet. On the other hand, it may be possible to triangulate the framing in such a way as to relieve the stresses at the joints, producing the equivalent in rotational form to the lamella system with horizontal and longitudinal ties. Fig. 78 shows an interesting example of this arrangement in tubular chrome-nickel steel, in which it can be seen how the horizontal rings take the side thrust of the diagonal members and maintain the shape of the dome. This aviary for high-flying birds in Rome has a diameter of 100 ft. and a height of 60 ft., and displays a particularly neat manner of connecting the tubular members at their points of intersection. Little advantage seems so far to have been taken of the strength of complete circular members, either in compression or tension, except in dome construction. A reinforced concrete engine shed, however, recently constructed in France, seems to take advantage of the functionally convenient circular plan to provide an economical structure. As shown in fig. 79 there are two circles of supporting columns, and the roof assumes the form of an inverted umbrella with bow-string struts thrusting between an external tension ring and an internal compression ring. The outer diameter is 437 ft. and the external walls, composed of pre-cast units, are completely non-structural.

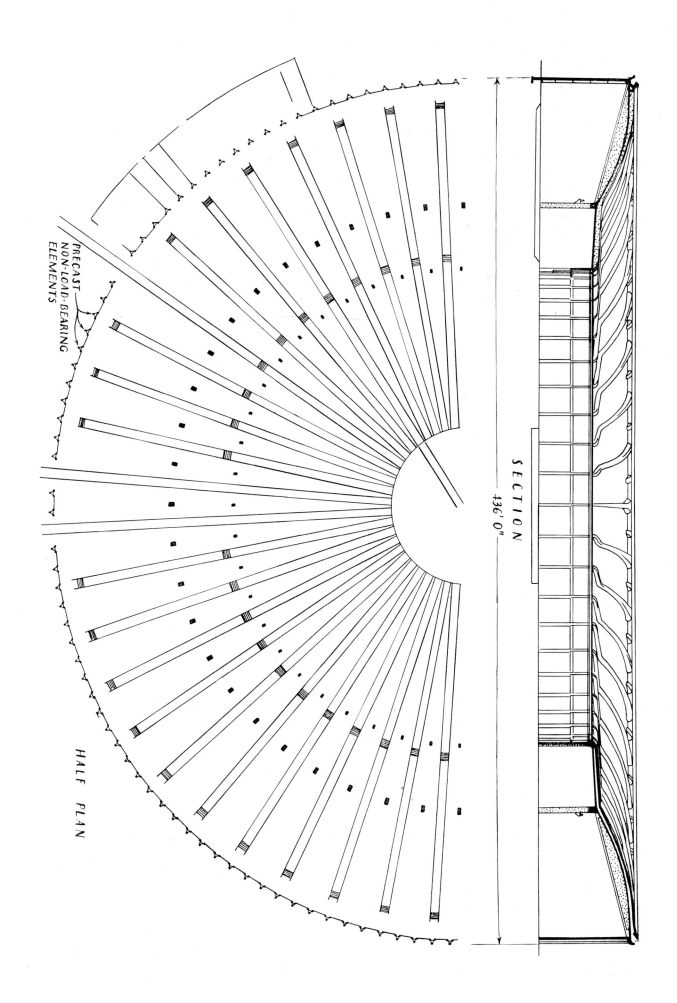

PRECAST NON-LOAD-BEARING ELEMENTS

SECTION
136' 0"

HALF PLAN

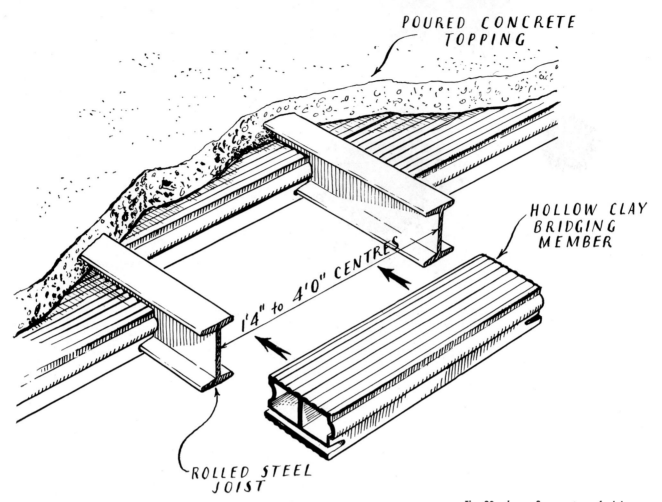

POURED CONCRETE
TOPPING

HOLLOW CLAY
BRIDGING
MEMBER

1'4" to 4'0" CENTRES

ROLLED STEEL
JOIST

Fig. 80, above, floor system of plain concrete spanning between steel joists.

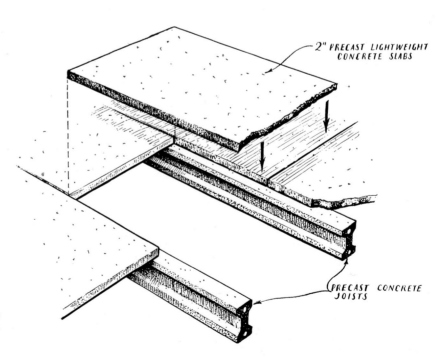

2" PRECAST LIGHTWEIGHT
CONCRETE SLABS

PRECAST CONCRETE
JOISTS

Fig. 81, right, floor system of thin reinforced
concrete slabs spanning between pre-cast
reinforced concrete joists.

The Horizontal Infilling

Since the function of structure is the collection of loads, which in normal architectural problems occur at any point on the horizontal plane, the skeleton frame is not an ideal structure as it needs to be complemented by the horizontal infilling. Of all structural components, the floor slab has perhaps been the subject of more patent systems than any. They are usually categorised according to the methods of construction—poured-in-place, combination of poured-in-place and pre-cast, or completely pre-cast. From a structural point of view, however, they can be divided into those which span in one direction and those which span in two directions.

Those spanning in one direction form the majority of existing systems. So long as steel was used predominantly in joist form, the filler joist system, i.e. breaking down the span into smaller spans which could be bridged with concrete, was the most obvious method, comparable with timber technique. Variations of this system are still in use, such as that in fig. 80, for joist spacing up to about 4 ft. For light loading the principle is also used in pre-cast reinforced concrete such as the example in fig. 81 where the thin bridging slabs of light weight concrete span between pre-cast concrete joists. With the predominant use of reinforced concrete, however, the tendency has been to keep the ribs at close centres to form a series of tee-beams side by side, so that all systems are virtually hollowed or ribbed floors sub-divided in some particular manner. The hollow floor offers the use of a compression flange

Systems spanning in one direction

71

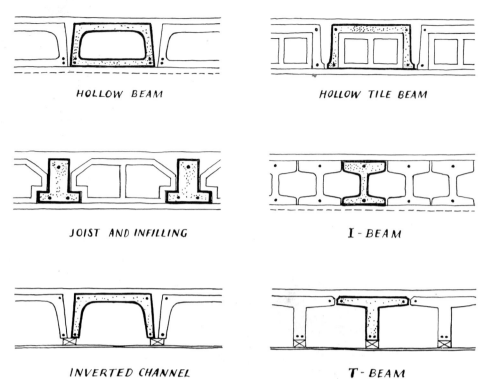

HOLLOW BEAM

HOLLOW TILE BEAM

JOIST AND INFILLING

I-BEAM

INVERTED CHANNEL

T-BEAM

Fig. 82, above right, some basic forms of pre-cast reinforced concrete floor units.

Fig. 83, below, a cored type of pre-stressed pre-cast reinforced concrete floor unit 6 inches deep, developed in the U.S.A. and designed to span up to 22 ft. for light loading.

Fig. 84, above and left, pre-stressed pre-cast reinforced concrete slabs produced in lengths of 300 ft. in Germany, are cut to required length. (Photo: British Crown Copyright Reserved.)

to resist negative moments over supports, and at the same time it gives a plain ceiling, improved sound and thermal insulation, and convenient service ducts. The pre-casting of units to be laid side by side seems to provide the biggest field for ingenuity, and the principal basic forms—joist, channel, box or tee-section—are shown in fig. 82. A span/depth ratio of 20 to 25 is considered reasonable for closely spaced joists of this type. Pre-stressed units have been developed in a number of countries using a cored section in addition to the more usual joist and channel types, and span/depth ratios with these units are considerably increased. A cored type which has been developed in the U. S. A. is shown in fig. 83; these units are 6 inches deep and capable of spanning up to 22 ft. for light loading. The reduced depth arising from pre-stressing provides the possibliity of widening the individual units into slab form, especially if light weight concrete is employed. In Germany at the end of World War II, such a slab was being produced in lengths of 300 ft., and subsequently cut according to requirements (fig. 84). Light weight pumice concrete was used around the steel and high grade concrete formed the com-pression flange.

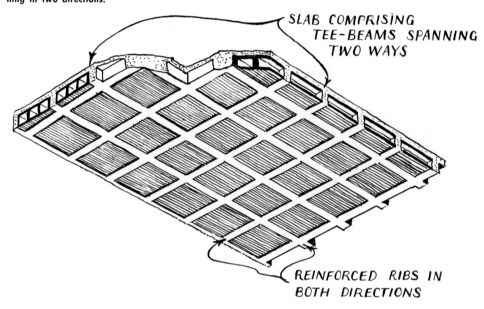

Fig. 85, below, hollow tile floor slab spanning in two directions.

SLAB COMPRISING
TEE-BEAMS SPANNING
TWO WAYS

REINFORCED RIBS IN
BOTH DIRECTIONS

**Use of the
infilling as an
active element**

Although the pre-cast units can be either freely supported or made continuous over several spans by grouting in continuity rods, all types using the cored or tee-beam principle must be considered as simple infillings spanning from beam to beam. The arousing of the floor slab to further structural duties is only effectively attained with the solid structural slab, which can form the compression flange of its supporting beam. So far this method has been applied almost entirely to reinforced concrete construction, but the possibilities of its use in steel frames, referred to in the Appendix, may eventually widen its application. The degree to which a heavy solid slab is warranted must obviously depend upon the percentage of slab which can be considered as a part of the supporting beam; the use of a lighter hollow section in that part of the slab which is not designed to operate as the compression flange of a supporting beam, is probably the most economical approach.

Fig. 86, above, pre- cast concrete floor panel with two-way ribs, manufactured by a vacuum process.

In the one-directional systems only a proportion of the framing beams carry floor loads, the remainder acting merely as ties and perhaps taking wind stresses. By spanning in two directions the load is not only distributed more evenly over the structure but a higher span/depth ratio is obtained in the slab. It is worth noting, however, that in practice it has sometimes been found that in terms of cost, the possible saving in the floor slab has been more than offset by the conversion of the ties into supporting beams. The two-way span is merely an interpretation of the rigid frame in the horizontal plane, and is dependent upon the co-operative action of all members in the frame. It has been mainly applied to larger spans, often in the form of a solid slab, but as in the one-way span, considerable weight can be saved by regarding it as a series of tee-beams spanning in both directions, with hollow blocks filling the squares in between (fig. 85). This form is also suitable for pre-cast slabs where the saving of weight is of such importance; the example shown in fig. 86 designed for manufacture by a vacuum process, has ribs at about 3 ft. centres and the concrete between ribs only 1¼" thick.

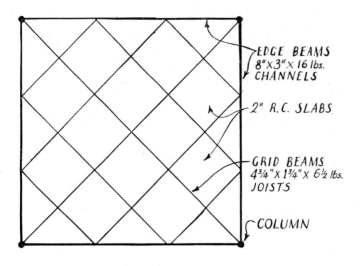

EDGE BEAMS
8"x3"x 16 lbs.
CHANNELS

2" R.C. SLABS

GRID BEAMS
4¾"x 1¾"x 6½ lbs.
JOISTS

COLUMN

PLAN

Fig. 87, left and below, diagonal grid floor
of welded steel joists four and three quarters inches deep spanning bays 20 ft.
square, in a factory at Yate, near Bristol,
England. Reinforced concrete slabs 2 inches
thick completed the infilling. (Engineers:
Diagrid Structures, Ltd.)

**Two-way span on
a diagonal grid**

The two-way method parallel to the framing grid is most advantageous in cases where bays are approximately square in shape, since the design of the slab will otherwise tend to be governed by the longer of the two spans. The alternative method, which overcomes this disadvantage, is to use a diagonal grid which reduces the span of the longest components. This system produces components or beams of different lengths and varying stiffness, the shorter ones acting as elastic supports for the longer ones. It seems to have been applied mainly to larger spans and on a fairly large grid with a two-way slab as infilling. For such spans it may permit a considerable saving in depth compared with a system of main and secondary beams, and it is particularly useful in the spanning of large bays where it is necessary that there should be a uniform height over the whole area. It has

Fig. 88, above and right, diagonal grid roof slab, 3½ ft. deep in reinforced concrete, spanning an area about 76 ft. wide at the Store Street Bus Station, Dublin. (Architect: Michael Scott. Engineers: Ove Arup and Partners.)

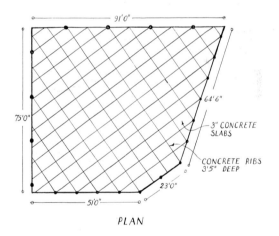

PLAN

been carried out in welded steel, as seen in fig. 87, where it forms the floor of a mezzanine divided into bays 20 ft. square, which was completed with a 2″ reinforced concrete infilling. It has probably been used more, however, in reinforced concrete, and a roof of considerable span has been constructed on this system at a Bus Station in Dublin (fig. 88). This roof provides a uniform height over the 76 ft. wide concourse and has an overall depth of about 3½ ft. The main disadvantage of this system lies in the large number of rigid joints which have to be made, involving a great deal of welding in the case of steel, and expensive formwork in the case of reinforced concrete, and although it may permit a saving of material, opinions about its overall economy seem to vary.

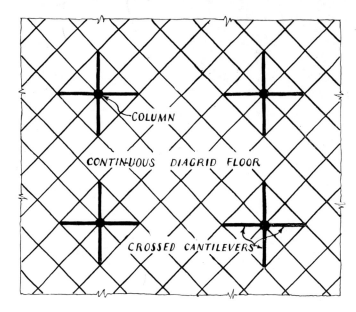

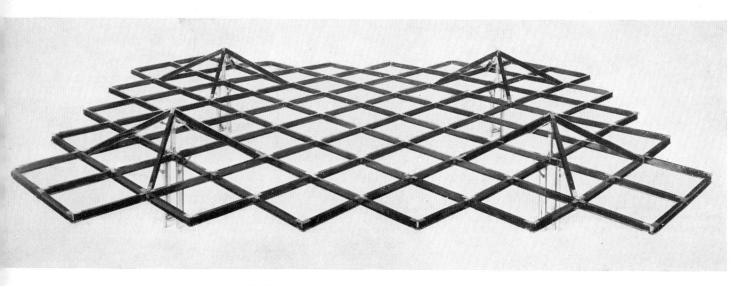

Fig. 89, left, plan of a typical internal bay of a diagonal grid system in which main supporting beams are replaced by crossed cantilevers, either above or below the column heads. (Engineers: Diagrid Structures, Ltd.)

Fig. 90, above, model of a typical bay of a diagonal grid roof in steel, showing the use of framed cantilevers over the supporting columns to eliminate all main beams. (Engineers: Diagrid Structures, Ltd.)

Elimination of main beams by means of continuity

The type of diagonal grid so far considered is that spanning between main beams supported on columns. In continuous construction of this sort, however, the edge beams can be replaced by cross cantilevers over the columns (fig. 89), either above or below the plane of the diagonal grid, and a proposed method carrying this out in steel is shown in fig. 90. The important point to notice is that some of the grid beams are unsupported along the lines connecting the columns, and we see the transition from column and beam to column and slab form. In reinforced concrete, soffit slabs may be provided at all corner panels to form the compression flanges of the cantilevers, or else these cantilevers will take the place of the drop panel and mushroom head characteristic of orthodox flat slab construction (see fig. 95). In fact, the system could be used as an alternative to mushroom construction by using a continuous soffit slab combined with suitable crosshead cantilevers.

Part 2

BEYOND THE SKELETON FRAME

The realisation of continuity and mutual support in framing members lends itself to an ultimate fusion in which the frame is transformed into an elastic diaphragm or slab. The ability to obtain such an element, by embedding in concrete steel reinforcing bars in lattice form, pointed the way to a new field in which contemporary materials could be used to develop structures beyond the linear conception of the skeleton frame. This development is of greatest significance in the spanning of space, since the principal loads on a structure are normally distributed in a horizontal plane and the slab form is therefore the most suitable for collecting them.

The early employment of the structural slab in the form of a horizontal diaphragm on point supports might be regarded as the interpretation in contemporary man-made materials of the post and beam conception—governed in the past by the form of nature-given structural materials — in so far as it relies on resistance to bending moments for the collection and transfer of loads. The limitations in span imposed by this conception seemed very soon to have led to the application of the principles of that other great invention of the past—arch or vault construction—in which the stresses are confined to direct forces in the plane of the arch itself. Thus, by the folding or arching of the structural diaphragm into suitable shape in such a way that bending moments are replaced to a great extent by direct forces in the plane of the slab, large areas can now be spanned with material of shell-like character. Moreover, these elements, which can be of great variety, may either be carried on point supports and thus retain the planning advantages of the skeleton frame, or they may form in themselves complete three-dimensional stressed-skin enclosures.

Although such forms of slab and shell construction are still in their infancy, they open up to the architect and engineer new fields of structural design, which when combined with those forms already considered, provide opportunities undreamed of in previous ages. It is in these forms that the full significance of contemporary structural development can best be appreciated.

Fig. 91, above, an arched reinforced concrete slab less than 6 inches thick forms the main structure of this 125 ft. span footbridge over the Toess near Wulflingen, Switzerland. Vertical slabs connect the arch to the 5½ inch thick platform and parapet walls, which stiffen the arch by resisting all bending moments. (Engineers: Robert Maillart and W. Pfeiffer.)

Fig. 92, left, the Schwandbach bridge near Schwarzenburg, Switzerland, of 123 ft. span, is a stiffened reinforced concrete arched slab structure, elliptical on plan. The use of a curved span was made possible by the slab form. (Engineer: Robert Maillart.)

Fig. 93, right, Langwies Bridge, Switzerland, constructed of beam and column superstructure supported on arch ribs.

The Structural Slab

It was Robert Maillart who was the first to show in practice that contemporary structural materials lend themselves to forms beyond the linear conception of skeleton framing members. He appreciated that reinforced concrete had greater possibilities than the beam and column form in which it had been introduced, and showed that it was possible to reinforce a flat concrete slab and support it on columns without the introduction of beams, and to stiffen a curved concrete slab in such a way that it could replace the solid arch ribs of bridge construction.[8] By means of a combined process of calculation and experiment, the reinforced concrete slab was transformed from a mere series of shallow beams into an active unified structural element, capable of being stressed in a variety of ways. Maillart's use of these slabs is perhaps best known in his bridge construction, in which they were developed into thin two-hinged curved arch diaphragms stiffened from above. The footbridge shown in fig. 91 has a shallow curved arch slab only 5½ inches thick over a span of 125 ft. It is connected by means of a series of vertical stiffening slabs to the platform which combines with the parapet walls to stiffen the arch and resist all bending moments. In another bridge (fig. 92) constructed on the same principle, the use of the slab form provided an admirable solution to the problem of a curved span over a mountain gorge, which with beam and arch construction would have had to be kept to a straight line owing to torsional stresses. Comparing these bridges with another example in Switzerland of normal reinforced concrete framed construction (fig. 93), the significance of these stiffened slab bridges and the architectural importance of the slab form itself, become apparent.

Maillart's contribution

[8]See Sigfried Giedion "Space, Time and Architecture" page 371. (Harvard University Press).

Fig. 94, left, first example in Europe of the horizontal slab on point supports, known as mushroom construction, was in the warehouse building at Zurich-Giesshubel, Switzerland, erected in 1910. (Engineer: Robert Maillart.)

The slab on point supports

Maillart's experiments with beamless flooring date from 1908, and the warehouse which he constructed in Zurich in 1910 (fig. 94) was the first example of mushroom construction in Europe. It was quite different in conception from the type constructed a little earlier in Minneapolis by the American engineer C. A. P. Turner. This was based on the extension of the column rods radially some four feet or more out into the slab and supporting on these ring rods, which in turn carried the lighter reinforcement for the slab construction. Although it is probable that there has been more flat slab construction in the U. S. A. than in any other country, except perhaps for the U.S.S.R., the design seems to have retained the one-dimensional idea of forces acting in independent directions requiring all reinforcing bars to pass over the supports, and hence rods were placed diagonally across the floor in addition to those parallel to the column grid, as though the slab was a series of intersecting beams. The forms of the mushroom columns therefore came to be of the drop-slab type as seen in fig. 95, which according to Maillart is wasteful in material since it does not agree with the natural flow of forces.[9] The real structural role of the slab is that of an elastic diaphragm reinforced according to stress distribution. These stresses, however, are difficult to determine by calculation alone, and experiment therefore formed a very important part in developing the theory of mushroom construction. In practice, approximate design methods have been evolved for which are laid down such things as the proportion and minimum number of bays, the location and dimensions of openings in the slab, methods of dealing with point loading, and the size of column heads. These conditions, however, are inclined to be more restricting than would be the case with a design based on more accurate analysis.

[9]See "The development of the beamless floor-slab in Switzerland and the U.S.A." in "Robert Maillart" by Max Bill (Verlag für Architektur AG—Erlenbach-Zürich).

Fig. 95, above, the form of mushroom construction developed in the U.S.A. employs a distributing or drop slab over the column heads as seen in the plant for Bond Stores, Inc. at Rochester, New York (Architect and Engineer: Albert Kahn, Associated Architects and Engineers, Inc.)

Fig. 96, below, a modified type of flat-slab construction used in the Fisher Cleveland bomber plant at Cleveland, Ohio. By reducing dead weight to a minimum, it was possible to space columns at about 50 ft. centres in both directions.

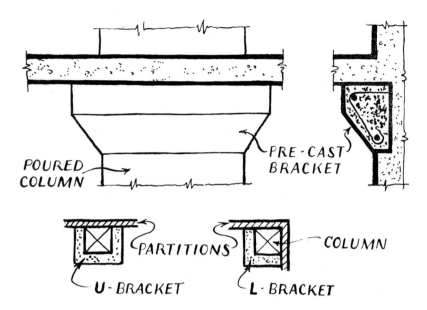

POURED COLUMN

PRE-CAST BRACKET

PARTITIONS

COLUMN

U-BRACKET

L-BRACKET

Fig. 97, left, pre-cast concrete column head developed for use in flat slab construction where loads demand additional column area to prevent the column head from punching through the slab. (Engineer: Fred N. Severud.)

Application of flat-slab construction

A survey carried out a few years ago in the U. S. A.[10] showed that of seven different types of floor in common use, flat slab construction used the smallest quantity of steel over a 20 ft. span with loading of 100 lbs./sq.ft. This loading is normally considered to be the minimum for economical use of flat slab design, with the economical span lying between 16 and 25 ft. The authors of the survey, however, have claimed that flat slab design will often show a saving both in cost and in quantity of steel for light load construction such as apartment buildings, and suggest that it deserves consideration in many other structures. Pre-stressing may reinforce this opinion by permitting a reduction in the dead weight of the slab as well as increasing the economical span, and a system of pre-stressed flat slab construction has actually been designed, though not yet carried out. The method employed in a plant at Cleveland, Ohio, to increase the span of a flat slab by reducing its dead weight, is shown in fig. 96. The dimensions of each bay are about 50 ft. square and the floor, which is 1 ft. 8 inches deep overall, is coffered to form a grid of seventeen inch deep ribs, leaving a top slab three inches thick; the coffers are filled in around the mushroom head where shear and moment are greatest, and the system is somewhat reminiscent of the transitional diagonal grid construction previously described, but in this instance the grid lines run parallel with the column rows.

[10]See report on survey of Portland Cement Association in Architectural Record, February, 1942.

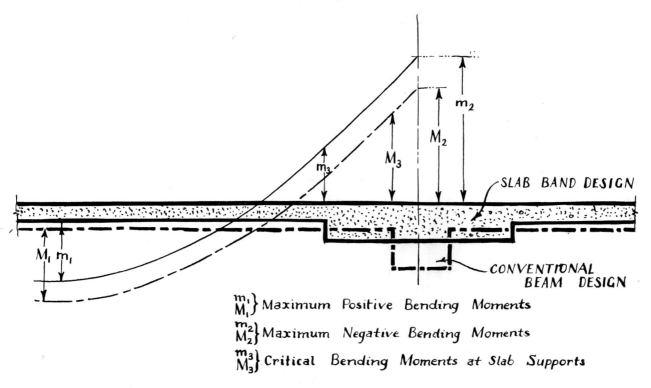

Fig. 98, below, comparison of stress distribution between conventional beam and slab construction and slab-band system, shows a better distribution in the latter case for critical stresses in the slab. (Engineer: Fred N. Severud.)

$\left.\begin{matrix} m_1 \\ M_1 \end{matrix}\right\}$ Maximum Positive Bending Moments

$\left.\begin{matrix} m_2 \\ M_2 \end{matrix}\right\}$ Maximum Negative Bending Moments

$\left.\begin{matrix} m_3 \\ M_3 \end{matrix}\right\}$ Critical Bending Moments at Slab Supports

The design of a flat slab over a column may be greatly influenced by the tendency of the column head to punch through the slab. On the other hand an enlarged column head does not always conform with planning requirements and the placing of steel column heads in the thickness of the slab, as has been done, for instance, in supporting roof slabs on tubular steel columns, is thought to be a possible means of overcoming this difficulty.[11] The other obvious solution is to keep the whole column to the size determined by punching shear, which in a multi-storey building would probably mean a uniform column size right up the building. It seems probable that the economy of this system would depend very much on the height of the building as this would determine the size of the largest column and the saving which could be effected by the standardisation of formwork. Another approach to the problem is to design the column head according to architectural requirements, and fig. 97 shows a proposal for a pre-cast type of head intended to increase the adaptability of flat slab construction by confining the head to two or three faces of the column.[12]

[11]See Fred N. Severud "Efficiency in Structure Invokes the Principle of Continuity" Architectural Record, January, 1946.

[12]See previous reference.

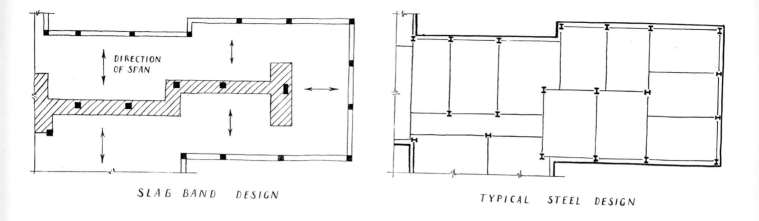

SLAB BAND DESIGN

TYPICAL STEEL DESIGN

The slab-band system

It is convenient to mention here a system which, whilst not embracing the conception of the flat slab diaphragm, employs a limited application of its principles and might approach it in appearance. Whilst the flat slab system absorbs the beam completely into the slab by means of a more uniform distribution of stresses in the horizontal plane, the flattening out of the beam into what has been called a slab-band, has been found to provide a closer relationship between material and stress distribution compared with a conventional beam and slab design. A drop slab in the flat slab system constitutes a haunch in the area of maximum stress which occurs over the column head, but since the stress distribution between columns is greater than that at panel centres, it may be convenient to go one step further and make the drop slabs continuous between column heads, thus breaking away from the diaphragm principle and creating, in effect, broad shallow beams or slab bands. The use of such flattened beams is equally applicable to one-way spans, and their closeness to the flat slab form seems to account for the better arrangement of material in relation to stress distribution than is the case with conventional beam design. Fig. 98 shows how the critical bending moments in the slab are reduced by virtue of the fact that the stiffness of the slab-band draws to itself increased negative moments; the latter can be conveniently resisted in the slab-band itself, with the lower part available as a compression area, and good use is therefore made of the available material. The savings which result from the reduction in slab thickness are said to outweigh the increase of steel in the slab-band and to make the system more economical than conventional beam and slab design.[13] The columns can be placed anywhere within the confines of the slab-band, but in cases of extremely eccentric loading, this might result in having to increase their size. This is apparently not usual, however, and in any case the principle of placing the column anywhere under the slab is claimed to be more economical than the normal method of introducing a new beam.

A comparison between a slab-band design and a normal steel frame layout is shown in fig. 99 to illustrate the difference in principle. In the slab-band system, the floor is treated as a continuous unit, with the band acting as a haunch, in the form of a flexible arm, which can be bent around corners as it passes from one column to the next, or cantilevered beyond them according to the nature of the plan.

[13]See Fred N. Severud "Why Slab-band Floors are Economical" Engineering News-Record, 17th October, 1946.

The horizontal slab is the logical structural form for the collection of loads occurring at any point in a horizontal plane. We have so far considered the horizontal slab on point supports which retains the essential advantages associated with skeleton framing, namely economy in floor space, flexible planning and a light structure. The horizontal slab, however, must resist forces perpendicular to its own plane and is therefore mainly subject to bending. Although this is clearly not the most efficient method of using the material in the slab, very little attention seems to have been given to the fact that much greater strength can be developed in the slab when used to resist forces in its own plane. It may be that its slenderness has been assumed to be a big disadvantage for using it in direct compression, but its effectiveness when suitably stiffened was amply demonstrated in the remarkably slender arched slabs used in some of Maillart's bridges. It may also have been thought that, since in this form the slab is no more than a flattened rib or column, there was no advantage to be gained in the use of a very slender member which, owing to its greater tendency to buckle under load, could only develop a reduced strength in the materials. Recent experiments, however, seem to have confirmed the belief that the slab in direct compression does not behave as though it were a flattened column. The tests which were carried out on a slab of unreinforced concrete 4 inches thick, showed that a far greater strength was developed in the material than would have been the case with a narrow column of equal thickness. It is thought that this is due to the compensating effect of the tendency of different parts of the slab to buckle in opposite directions. It seems therefore that the slab which is cross-reinforced so as to be a monolithic whole, is a structural element having its own characteristics when used in compression, just as it has when used in bending.

The use of the vertical slab as a structural element has been very limited so far, and the transfer of loads has been thought of only in terms of the point support provided by the skeleton frame, or the distributed support of the non-tensile load-bearing wall. Multi-storey structures have of necessity been confined to the point support, whilst structures up to three or four storeys have continued to make use of the load-bearing wall. Skeleton framing, therefore, became part of the ritual of multi-storey buildings even where the latter were unable to benefit from its essential advantages. At the same time the cumbersome nature of the load-bearing wall was accepted up to the point where its thickness became uneconomical. Recent years, however, have seen the vertical tensile slab beginning to take its place in building.

The slab as a compression member

The vertical slab

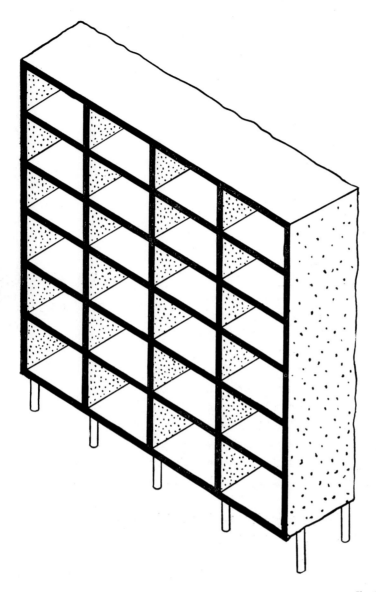

Fig. 100, left, structural system of horizontal and vertical slabs known as "box-frame" construction.

"Box-frame" construction

The term "box frame" is essentially a misnomer, as the word "frame" has become associated with a skeleton type of structure, i.e., with one dimensional elements. The term has come into use, however, to indicate a structure composed of vertical and horizontal slabs (fig. 100), and it is therefore proposed to employ it in these remarks. It was used before World War II in Copenhagen and elsewhere, and has been employed in the construction of a number of post-war apartment blocks in England. Fig. 101 shows one of these blocks at Rosebery Avenue, London, which is a typical example of the application of the system to superimposed dwellings. The cut-away view shows clearly how the thin structural walls form the space divisions in each apartment, eliminating the unsightly projections which accompany beam and column construction.

Fig. 103, above, constructional view of the box-frame structure in an apartment building at Daneswood Avenue, Lewisham, London, shows how the wall slabs can become cantilevers if required. (Architects: Maxwell Fry and Jane Drew. Engineers: Ove Arup and Partners.)

The system described is essentially based upon a simple structural grid of cross walls, leaving the ends of the boxes to be filled in with a great degree of flexibility and also permitting a high degree of standardisation. There may be cases, however, where planning requirements make it more convenient to use the structural slabs longitudinally, forming external as well as internal walls, although this method increases the problem of providing a suitable finish or facing to the structural wall. An example of this kind is an apartment block at Highgate, London, (fig. 104), where external walls of 6 inch reinforced concrete slabs were used in conjunction with an internal spine of beams and columns. The structure is obviously much less rigid in this form, and must rely to a considerable extent on the stiffness imparted by the end cross-walls, which in this case are also of monolithic construction.

Fig. 104, above and right, in the Highpoint 1 apartment building at Highgate, London, the external walls of 6 inch reinforced concrete slabs combine with an internal spine to form the structure. (Architects: Tecton. Engineers: J. L. Kier and Co., Ltd.)

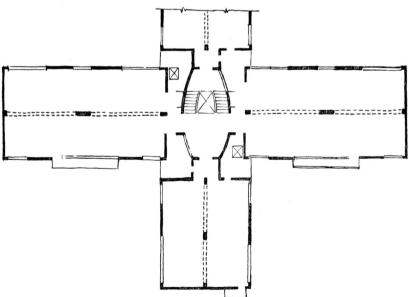

TYPICAL UPPER FLOOR PLAN SHOWING
MAIN STRUCTURAL ELEMENTS

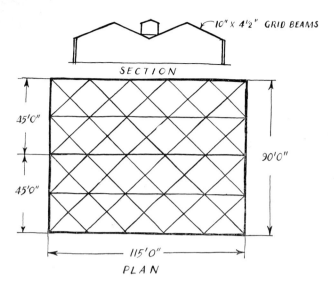

SECTION

10" X 4'2" GRID BEAMS

45'0"

45'0"

90'0"

115'0"

PLAN

Fig. 105, above and right, folded type of rigid diagonal framing in welded steel, tied only at each end of the 115 ft. span, used to roof a factory at Yate near Bristol, England. (Engineers: Diagrid Structures, Ltd.)

Folding of the horizontal slab

Although the vertical slab can be considered as a deep beam if necessary, beyond a certain point it will be uneconomical as a beam alone, since it requires adequate thickness for flexural rigidity, but at the same time only the extreme fibres are stressed to the permissible limits. On the other hand, the same slab turned on its side into the horizontal plane has a much smaller moment of resistance and flexural rigidity. Between these two limits there is the folded slab, consisting of elements disposed in diagonal planes, rigidly connected and providing mutual assistance; this provides a more economical stressing of material together with a useful roofing form. As with the flat slab, the derivative form can be obtained with rigidly connected framing members, executed either in welded steel or reinforced concrete. The space frame described earlier (see fig. 24) is based on the same principle, but not being of rigid construction, the folded form can only be maintained by means of a system of bracing and ties throughout the length of the frame. On the other hand, the saw-tooth girders of 125 ft. span shown in fig. 23 are rigidly inter-connected at their junctions and maintain the shape of the roof planes, assisted only by the ties of the main girders. A folded type of roof constructed of rigidly connected diagonal framing members is shown in fig. 105. The roof of this factory near Bristol, England, which has a span of 115 feet, uses 10 inch deep steel joists in the roof planes, welded at their points of intersection, and the only ties which are provided are at the ends of the span. It is clear that the structural effect of the folding process is to increase greatly the ratio between the span and the depth of the actual structural plane, but this is done only as a result of a big increase in the overall constructional depth.

93

SECTIONAL PERSPECTIVE VIEW

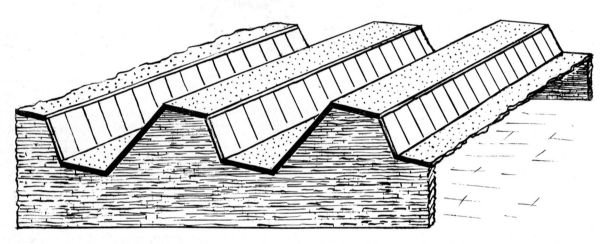

Fig. 106, above, a type of folded slab roof designed for the profile of a saw-tooth roof.

Forms of folded slab

Just as the flat horizontal slab is the limiting case of the rigid frame in the horizontal plane, so the ultimate development of the folded structure composed of rigidly connected members is a system of folded slabs. The use of the slab in this manner enables considerable spans to be achieved in the direction of the folds with a comparatively thin slab, since the structural shape results in the setting up of substantial forces within the planes of the folds, and this, as noted previously, is the most efficient method of stressing the slab. The folds can be arranged in a variety of ways and in any required number, providing a very direct method of obtaining a particular roof profile. The saw-tooth is probably the most common in industrial structures, and fig. 106 shows a type of folded slab roof designed for this profile which has been used in a number of factories for spans up to 70 feet. Fig. 107

Fig. 107, above and left, saw-tooth type roof at the factory for Messrs. Gestetner, Tottenham, London, is constructed of folded reinforced concrete slabs about 4 inches thick, spanning about 40 ft. between supporting frames. (Architects: Tecton. Engineer: J. L. Kier and Co., Ltd.)

Fig. 108, above and right, trough-shaped reinforced concrete slabs of polygonal form and only 3 inches thick, span 37.5 ft. between supporting frames in a workshop attached to the Aircraft Assembly Hall at Filton near Bristol, England. (Architect: Eric Ross. Engineers: The British Reinforced Concrete Engineering Co., Ltd.)

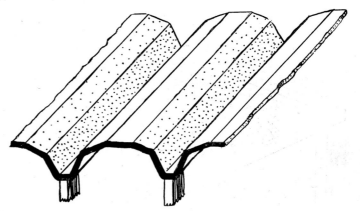

Fig. 109, right, polygonal vaults in reinforced concrete simplify the formwork, but use more material than true arch forms, owing to the increased moments at the folds.

shows a London factory with a roof of this type, which has a span of about 40 feet between supporting frames, and a slab thickness of about 4 inches. A more unusual type was used in the roof of a workshop near Bristol, England. As seen in fig. 108 this consists of a series of trough-shaped elements connected at intervals by ribs which transmit the stresses between the sloping sides of the troughs. The roof spans a distance of 37½ feet between main beams with a slab thickness of 3 inches. The use of a larger number of folds makes it possible to approach more closely to a true shell construction (see later), and the polygonal form of vault as shown in fig. 109 may be a convenient compromise since it simplifies the formwork; on the other hand, it requires the use of more steel and concrete owing to the increase of bending moments at the folds, in the same way as the rigid frame uses more material than the true arch form, and for this reason it has apparently been limited so far to fairly small spans.

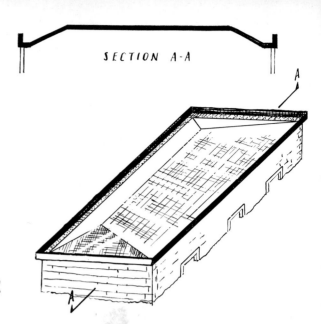

Fig. 110, right, hipped form of roof with continuous support, for which thin sheet materials could be used.

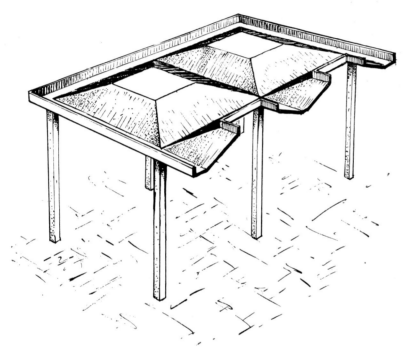

Fig. 111, left, hipped roofs square on plan are more suitable if point supports are required.

The hipped form of folded slab

If the stresses in the slab roof are to be kept to a minimum, it is necessary to introduce frames or stiffeners at the ends of each span to maintain the folded shape (in the case of the two examples illustrated, the supporting beams perform this function). One method of doing this is to provide hips so that the slab becomes folded in two directions, producing a structural element with a perimeter all in one plane. This type of element could be very suitable where continuous support can be provided around the whole roof perimeter, as shown in fig. 110, and it is a form which lends itself to the application of thin sheet materials such as sheet metal. There is no reason, however, why point supports should not be used, but the most economical shape would then seem to be a hipped slab which is square on plan, as in fig. 111, since this has the advantage of providing the benefits of a two-way span. In fact it can then be compared to a flat slab system where each bay is pressed up into a hollow polygonal hipped shape, permitting a far greater load to be carried than in its original form.

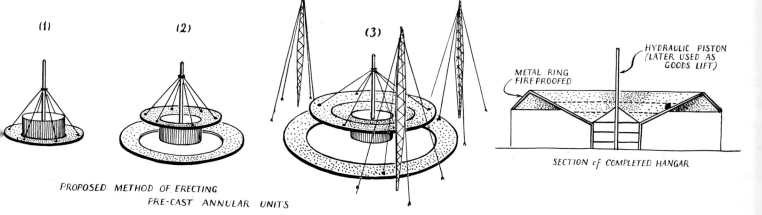

Fig. 112, below, project for an inverted umbrella type of hangar roof, constructed of annular pre-cast concrete units with external tension ring. (Engineer: Fred N. Severud.)

(1)　　**(2)**　　　**(3)**

HYDRAULIC PISTON
(LATER USED AS
GOODS LIFT)

METAL RING
FIREPROOFED

PROPOSED METHOD OF ERECTING
PRE-CAST ANNULAR UNITS

SECTION of COMPLETED HANGAR

The complete dome can be a particular case of the folded slab in the form of a flat cone. It is particularly useful with a central support and inverted cone, with the outside ring reinforcement resisting lateral thrust, so that the action of the load is like that of pressing down on a stiffened plunger. A suggested hangar design based on the erection of such a structure from pre-cast units is shown in fig. 112; the units are cast on the ground and hoisted in annular sections. This umbrella type of structure seems to be very suitable for smaller types of shelter where an unobstructed outer perimeter is desirable. A similar form, but with additional stiffening ribs, was used for the mushroom columns (fig. 113) in the building at Racine mentioned previously and is being employed on a much larger scale in the floors of a Laboratory Tower extension for the same company (fig. 114), which form an annular cantilever of about 15 feet around the central supporting core. Considerable loads can be sustained by such circular structures taking advantage of the stiffness imparted to the slab by its circular shape and the inherent strength of the complete ring in tension. Other forms can be developed by using a tensile skin and a compressive ring.

**The rotational
folded slab**

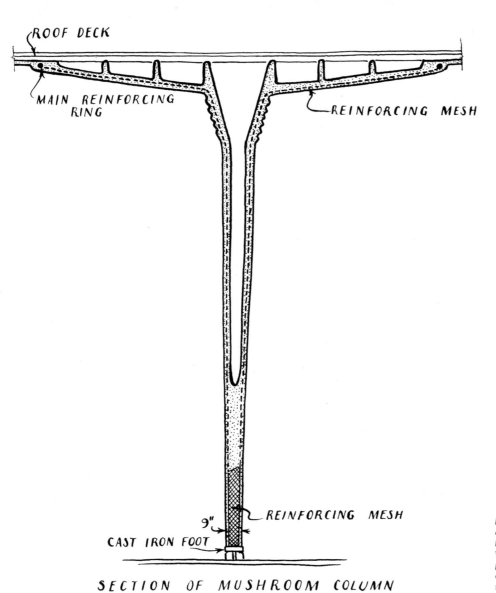

ROOF DECK

MAIN REINFORCING RING

REINFORCING MESH

REINFORCING MESH

9"

CAST IRON FOOT

SECTION OF MUSHROOM COLUMN

Fig. 113, left and below, mushroom-head of the columns used in the Administration Building, Johnson Wax Company, Racine, Wisconsin, is comparable to an inverted plunger with stiffened concrete compression area and steel tension ring to resist lateral thrust. (Architect: Frank Lloyd Wright.)

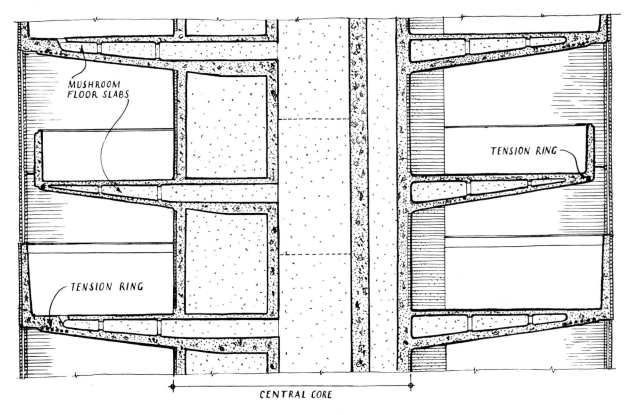

MUSHROOM
FLOOR SLABS

TENSION RING

TENSION RING

CENTRAL CORE

PART CROSS SECTION

Fig. 114, above and below, each floor of the Laboratory Tower for the Johnson Wax Company at Racine, Wisconsin, is constructed on the same principle as the heads of the mushroom columns in the Administration Building, giving an annular cantilever of about 15 ft. from the central supporting core. (Architect: Frank Lloyd Wright.)

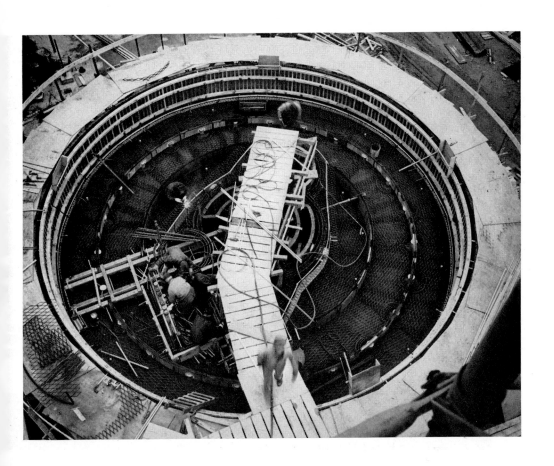

The Structural Shell

Nature of the structural shell

Whilst the strength of the slab in its own plane can be used to great effect in the transfer of loads, the use of the slab for load collection is most effective in its folded form, since forces may thereby be set up in the planes of the folds, thus reducing the internal bending moments. In the arched form of folded slab (see fig. 109), the limiting case with an infinite number of folds is the barrel vault, and by choosing certain shapes for the barrel, loads can be transmitted by means of direct forces in the surface of the vault with internal bending moments, for all practical purposes, non-existent.

This replacement of bending moments by direct forces, will normally result in a considerable economy of material, and the curved slab into which the structural element is developed can therefore be extremely thin, comparable with a shell. At the same time, the curved shape, like arched forms in skeleton framing, normally limits the use of the structural shell to the solution of roofing problems, and it is especially suitable where spans are large or there is much repetition. The fact that the shell itself can be extremely thin makes it possible to use various sheet materials, and shells have been constructed of sheet steel and hardboard, but reinforced concrete is the material mainly used for this form of construction. In fact it is only in this form that reinforced concrete has become suitable for large spans, as a result of the efficient way in which the material is stressed. Although preliminary work on the development of shell construction was started at the beginning of the century, the general theory was apparently not arrived at until about 1927, so that the structural shell is still, relatively speaking, in its infancy.

Characteristics

The shell is merely a development of the structural slab, which by forming the latter into appropriate shape, makes a more efficient use of the ability of the slab, when suitably reinforced, to transmit loads in more than one direction simultaneously. The first requirement is that suitable framing or stiffening should be provided, to maintain the shell in the desired shape; it can then be reinforced in such a way that it can be used to transmit loads along the length as well as across the breadth of the shell surface. In the case of the single curved shell or barrel vault, this means that the shell can span as a beam along the length of the barrel and is a completely self-contained structural element. It therefore differs from the arch vaults of non-tensile materials—which, transmitting forces only in the direction of curvature, require continuous support along their edges—in the same respect as the flat slab on point supports differs from beam and slab construction. In the case of shells

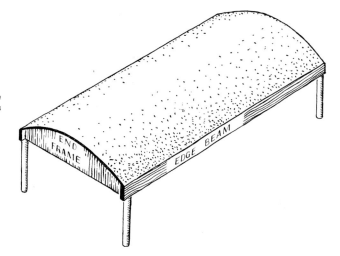

Fig. 115, right, the shell spans as a beam between end frames which maintain its shape.

curved in two directions, the only previously comparable construction was the dome, which as mentioned later becomes freed of many restrictions which accompanied its construction out of small non-tensile units.

In shell construction, the structure itself forms the roof enclosure and since the required thickness increases only at a very low rate and between certain limits may even be governed by considerations other than the direct stresses involved, the dead weight of the whole roof does not increase appreciably as spans become larger. This is of particular importance in long span construction where dead weight is normally a very big factor. On the other hand, formwork assumes greater importance in the case of the shell, so that it might be cheaper for smaller spans to revert to the folded type of structure having a number of planes in cross-section, although more material is used in this way. Again, although there may be a very high saving in steel compared with an equivalent steel skeleton frame, the form-work is likely to be of equal importance in the comparison of overall economy in any given case. The great accuracy required in the form-work is shown by the specification for the dome of the Hayden Planetarium in New York, which required that it should not differ from a true sphere by more than ½ inch at any point.

The shell of single curvature

The single-curved shell lends itself to the greatest repetition, since it normally permits the division of an area into a number of oblong bays. As previously indicated, this barrel type of shell spans as a beam between end-frames which rigidly maintain its curved shape (fig. 115). In the case of a semi-circular or elliptical barrel, where the tangents to the sides of the vaults are vertical, there is no tendency for the shell to burst outwards at the edges, and in fact the ideal shape of the barrel, theoretically, is similar to an ellipse. The constructional depth of such barrels is usually too great, however, and so it is usual to employ arcs of circles with rectangular edge-beams acting as stiffeners and ties (fig. 115). The edge-beam is an integral part of the shell and in most cases would be incapable of carrying even its own weight to the columns. The composite member of shell and edge-beam is comparable to a tee-beam, with the shell as compression flange and edge-beam as tension rib, but it is more efficient, owing to its shape. In some cases the edge-beams have been pre-stressed by means of non-bonded cables; this reduces the compression stresses in the loaded shell and may enable a thinner shell to be used or the constructional depth to be reduced.

Fig. 116, above, steel ties are used to maintain the shape of the reinforced concrete shell roof in this warehouse for Messrs. Colodense, Ltd., at Bristol, England. (Architect: E. F. Peat. Engineer: F. J. Samuely.)

Fig. 117, left, stiffening ribs used to maintain the shape of the 2½ inch thick barrel vault shells in a factory for Enfield Cables, Ltd. at Brynmawr, Wales. (Architects: Architects' Co-operative Partnership. Engineers: Ove Arup and Partners.)

Fig. 118, below, left and right, a pre-stressed reinforced concrete beam of 190 ft. span acts as an end-frame support to the 130 ft. span pre-stressed cylindrical roof shells in this hangar at the airport of Karachi, Pakistan. (Engineers: J. C. Gammon, Ltd. under licence from the Pre-stressed Concrete Co., Ltd.)

Fig. 119, above, timber sheds at Speke, Liverpool, England, constructed of 55 ft. span barrel shells supported on and stiffened by rigid frames. Angular thickening at the barrel intersections replaces internal edge beams. (Engineers: W. K. Wallace and Messrs. Chisarc and Shell 'D'.)

Although it seems to be more usual, it is not essential to carry the shells on point support, and therefore as with the horizontal slab, load transfer can be by means either of columns or of slabs. The nature of the end-frame or stiffening of the shell will depend to some extent on the method of supporting it and on the spacing of columns, where these are used for support. A rather special case is shown in fig. 116 where steel ties are used, but the span of the shell between columns is very small in this case, having been governed by existing columns. Another method is shown in fig. 117 where small stiffening ribs are inserted at the ends of each of the 53 ft. span barrel vaults. The ultimate form of the stiffening rib is the rigid frame as seen in fig. 119. It may be convenient to have a solid end frame as seen in fig. 115, or alternatively lighting requirements may dictate the use of a trussed type such as was used at one end of the shells in the hangar at Karachi Airport (fig. 118). This hangar also illustrates a case where a large span was required at one end of the barrel vaults. This meant supporting all the barrels on a single end-frame, which spans as a beam across the hangar opening 190 ft. wide. The roof structure consists of 2½ inch thick cylindrical shells, each 35 ft. wide with pre-stressed edge-beams, and spanning 130 ft. with a total constructional depth of 13 ft. The barrels are supported on columns at 35 ft. centres at one end and are carried at the other end by pre-stressed I-section beams 22 ft. deep in the centre and 16 ft. at the supports, spanning 190 ft. over the door openings; special provision is made for expansion. It will be noted that the span/depth ratio of the barrel and edge-beam is exactly ten, i.e. about the same as for an average steel lattice girder and this is the desirable ratio for simply supported spans greater than about 60 ft. Sometimes the rise of the barrel is sufficient to achieve this without the addition of edge-beams, in which case the angular intersection of the barrels provides sufficient stiffness for the shell. The timber sheds at Speke, Liverpool (fig. 119), having two spans of 55 ft., are of this type.

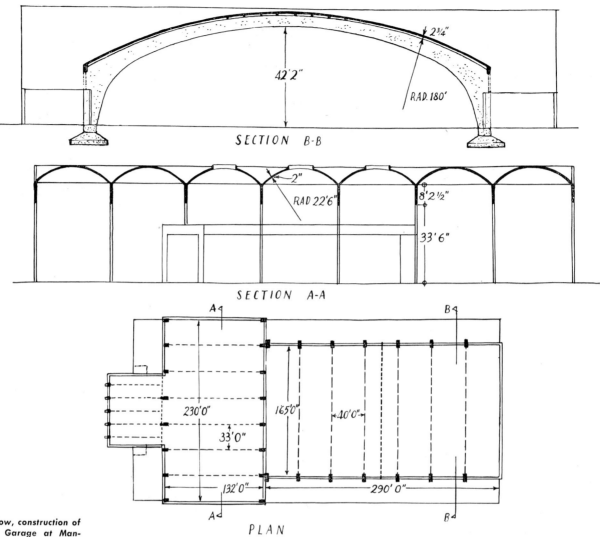

42'2"

2¾"

RAD.180'

SECTION B-B

RAD 22'6"

2"

8'2½"

33'6"

SECTION A-A

A

B

230'0"

165'0"

40'0"

33'0"

132'0"

290'0"

A

B

PLAN

Fig. 120, above and below, construction of the Wythenshawe Bus Garage at Manchester, England, illustrates the two contrasting types of barrel vault shell. The main garage has barrels 175 ft. wide spanning between two-hinged arches at 40 ft. centres. (Architect: G. Noel Hill. Engineers: H. G. Cousins and Messrs. Chisarc and Shell 'D'.)

Fig. 121, right, the reinforced concrete shell roof of the U. S. Army hangar at Rapid City, South Dakota, has a clear span of 340 feet with a shell thickness varying from five to seven inches. Main arch ribs are tied at the feet with pre-tensioned steel rods. (Engineers: Roberts and Schaefer Co.)

Where the shape of the barrel vault approximates an arc of a circle, it is considered that a length which is approximately twice the width is likely to give the most economical proportions for the shell, and in any case it is undesirable to make the shell too slender. The radius is usually made somewhat less than the width and most examples are said to fall between a very long barrel having a length of six times the radius and a very short one having a length of one sixth of the radius.[15] The actual dimensions themselves are limited and 50 feet has been suggested as the maximum probable width, while the necessity to provide expansion joints seems to limit the length of the barrel between end-frames to about 200 ft. Above this span it is necessary to use a short type of barrel having a width equal to the span required and supported on arch ribs which act as end frames. It may even be more economical to adopt this method below a span of 200 ft. The two contrasting types are well illustrated in the bus garage at Manchester, England (fig. 120), which is partly covered by long barrels 132 ft. by 33 ft. and partly by short barrels 165 ft. wide and 2¾ inches thick spanning as a continuous beam over two-pin arches placed at 40 ft. centres. The arch ribs in this case are placed inside the shell, whereas in the 294 ft. span hangar at San Diego previously illustrated (fig. 55), which has short barrel shells of the same type 3½ inches thick, the ribs were placed externally, facilitating the use of movable formwork. A more recent hangar of similar construction at Rapid City, S. Dakota (fig. 121) has a clear span of 340 feet with shells varying from 5 to 7 inches in thickness spanning across arch ribs placed about 25 feet apart. The arch, as can be seen, is a very flat one and part of the enormous lateral thrust from the arch ribs is taken up by sets of six 2½ inch pretensioned steel rods placed between the footings of each arch rib. This hangar was finished with a one inch insulating blanket below the composition roofing but the insulation can equally well be incorporated in the shell itself by constructing it of light-weight concrete. The shell in that case would normally be thicker than one constructed with dense concrete owing to a reduction in the strength of the material.

[15]See H. G. Cousins "Shell Concrete Construction"—paper read to the Reinforced Concrete Association, London, in January, 1948.

Fig. 122, left, the reinforced concrete shell vault spanning over rigid frames in this hangar at Cologne, Germany, is of asymmetrical form to permit a high door opening on one side.

Fig. 123, right, stiffening ribs, reminiscent of sea shells, appear between the main supporting arches of a shell-roofed hangar at Cologne, Germany.

Fig. 124, left, saw-tooth shells span 35 ft. between the 16 ft. deep main beams which give a clear floor span of about 155 ft. in this hangar in Algeria.

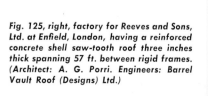

Fig. 125, right, factory for Reeves and Sons, Ltd. at Enfield, London, having a reinforced concrete shell saw-tooth roof three inches thick spanning 57 ft. between rigid frames. (Architect: A. G. Porri. Engineers: Barrel Vault Roof (Designs) Ltd.)

Fig. 126, above, a garage at Nuremberg in which the roof shells are of double canti-lever type with cross-head cantilever end-frames above the shell, permitting continu-ous glazing 10 ft. wide down the center of each bay.

Fig. 127, right, aerial view of the platform roof at Northolt Station, England, shows the cross-head cantilever supporting frames of the double cantilever shell roof. (Engineers: Barrel Vault Roof (Designs) Ltd.)

Types of asymmetrical barrel vault

It is possible for the shape of the barrel to be unsymmetrical, which makes it useful in hangar construction where a high door opening may be required on one side as shown in a hangar at Cologne, Germany (fig. 122). In large spans it may sometimes be desirable to insert small stiffening ribs familiar in sea shells, in order to achieve the required local strength without thickening the whole of the shell; this can be seen in another hangar at Cologne (fig. 123). The unsymmetrical barrel is particularly useful in providing a roof shape suitable for a good distribu-tion of light, such as the saw-tooth type.

In a hangar in Algeria (fig. 124), an even distribution of light was required over the whole floor area even when the doors were closed and the method adopted was to use a series of saw-tooth shells about 2¾ inches thick which span 35 feet between the 16 ft. deep main beams; the latter provide a clear floor span of about 155 feet. A more usual application is seen in a factory in London (fig. 125) where the 3 inch thick saw-tooth shells have a span of 57 ft. and are this time supported between rigid frames of fairly small span. This arrangement provides a minimum obstruction to light and owing to the reflections from the curved shell surface, the standard of light that can be obtained with this form of saw-tooth roof, is very high. Another application of the asymmetrical shell is seen in a garage at Nurem-berg, Germany (fig. 126) where the roof shells are of double cantilever type span-ning between cross-head cantilever end-frames above the shell; by this means a continuous strip of glazing 10 feet wide is obtained down the centre of each bay. The form of such double cantilevered end-frames is seen in fig. 127 which shows the application of the same system to the platform canopy of a railway station in England.

Fig. 128, above, exterior view of a factory at Aulnay sous Bois, France, shows the saw-tooth roof of conoidal type shells obtained by varying the rise of the barrel whilst maintaining a constant width.

Fig. 129, above, interior view of a conoidal shell saw-tooth factory roof in France shows the bow-string trusses which maintain the shape of the shells.

Another type of saw-tooth roof which has been used to some extent both in Western Europe and in South America, is obtained from the use of symmetrical shells with glazing between the ends of successive barrels. By diminishing the rise of the shell while maintaining its width, a series of interpenetrating conoidal shapes can be formed with vertical glazing at the intersections, as can be seen in a factory in France (fig. 128). The interior of another factory of the same type (fig. 129), shows how the shape of these shells is maintained by means of bow-string trusses, and how the shape itself is such that the sides of the shell remain horizontal. The tilting of the whole shell, however, is the method used in the roof of an industrial plant at Resiotencia, in the Argentine (fig. 130), where apparently this form of saw-tooth roof is widely used. The proportion of the shells is quite different in this case and it is probable that more uniform lighting is obtained from this method of arranging them. This system has also been used in South Africa with shells of uniform cross-section giving glazed areas bounded by the parallel curves of successive shells.

Fig. 130, above, saw-tooth roof of an industrial plant at Resiotencia, Argentina, formed of a series of tilted reinforced concrete shells.

Fig. 131, right, circular openings cut into the barrel vault roof shells provide the natural lighting in this bakery at Eastleigh, England. (Architects: A. J. Seal and Partners. Engineers: Barrel Vault Roof (Designs) Ltd.)

Provision of daylight

Where it is not convenient to obtain lighting by appropriate shaping or arrangement of the shells themselves, a reasonable standard of daylight can be obtained by piercing the shell surfaces. This may be done by means of rectangular apertures usually placed down the centre of the barrel vault, or by means of circular openings as seen in fig. 131 which can be conveniently covered by small glass domes and provide a more uniform distribution of light. Alternatively glass lenses may be built into the shell at regular intervals.

Although shell construction can be very competitive in cost for large spans compared with other forms of construction and in certain cases has even proved to be so for smaller spans, it seems unlikely to be cheaper initially for very small spans than conventional steel trusses with sheet roofing unless there is sufficient repetition. Even in these cases, however, the difference may not be found to be appreciable if reduced maintenance is taken into account. In general it appears that the cost is likely to rise as the span increases, mainly as a result of loss of repetition in the form-work.[16] It is not surprising, therefore, that attention has been given to the pre-casting of small span shells and this was developed in Germany during World War II where units about 16 feet by 33 feet were mass produced.

[16]See H. G. Cousins—reference above.

Fig. 133, right, dovetailed steel sheeting used in a prototype steel floor slab at King's Cross, London.

Fig. 132, left, barrel vaults over a canteen for Messrs. May & Baker at Dagenham, England, are cantlievered beyond their end frames. (Architect: Edward D. Mills. Engineers: Barrel Vault Roof (Designs) Ltd.)

Use of materials other than reinforced concrete

The importance assumed by the cost of formwork for shells constructed in reinforced concrete, leads to the consideration of the use of other materials for constructing the shells, especially those produced in sheet form. The big disadvantage of steel seems to be its great density, so that in slab form it can only be economically used in direct compression when suitably stiffened, since an adequate thickness to resist buckling would make the structure both costly and heavy. In its stiffened form, however, it has been used in the construction of barrel vaults for the roofs of hangars in France. One of these, which is at Cazau, has a roof of steel barrel vaults, approximately semi-circular in section, built out of welded steel plate stiffened on the underside by lattice ribs and angle-stiffeners. The shells have a span of about 110 feet between plate girders and were erected as units complete with end-frames after assembly on the ground. The other way of using steel would be in the form of lattice construction but fabrication costs are likely to be high and it was this reason, for instance, which resulted in the adoption of a modified form of steel design for the hangar referred to in the next chapter (see fig. 161). The use of 3/16 inch hardboard has also been tried in an experimental barrel vault roof having a span of 20 feet, but although it successfully withstood the necessary loading, it apparently did not reach the required standard of economy.

Fig. 134, above and right, a 2½ inch thick corrugated shell in reinforced concrete cantilevers 20 ft. to form a protective canopy at the Store Street Bus Station, Dublin. (Architect: Michael Scott. Engineers: Ove Arup and Partners.)

Corrugated form of single-curved shell

The barrel vault can be used as a continuous beam and it can equally well be cantilevered beyond its supports as seen in fig. 132. Since, however, the barrel vault is comparable to a tee-beam, it seems reasonable that the most efficient form of cantilever should be an inverted barrel, reversing areas of tension and compression. An alternation of barrels and inverted barrels, which produces a corrugated form, is therefore capable of acting both as a beam and a cantilever. It is common knowledge that any kind of corrugation will increase the stiffness of a slab, as for example in sheeting of corrugated iron or asbestos, and for reasons previously mentioned, the only economical way in which steel alone can be used as a slab either in bending or in compression, is in a corrugated form as seen in the floor shown in fig. 133. The corrugated form, however, seems so far to have been little exploited on a larger scale, but it appears to have considerable possibilities in shell construction, since it provides the flow of a continuous element capable of wider application than adjacent barrels stiffened at the junctions, and the possibility of using flexible form-work, capable of taking up the required shape under the action of gravity. Fig. 134 shows an example of the corrugated shell used as a cantilever to form a protective canopy at a bus station in Dublin; with an overall depth of only 2½ feet, the 2½ inch thick reinforced concrete shell is cantilevered a distance of 20 feet from its supporting beam.

Fig. 135, above and right, a special case of the shell curved in two directions is the arched corrugated structure used in the airship hangars at Orly, France, which have a span of 320 ft. and a rise of 195 ft. (Engineer: E. Freyssinet.)

CUTAWAY VIEW

The arch of corrugated section

If a corrugated section is arched, the stiffness is further increased, producing a particular case of the second type of shell, namely that curved in two directions. Perhaps the earliest application of this principle was in the airship hangars at Orly, France. One of these, having a span of 320 ft. and a rise of 195 ft. is shown in fig. 135; the serrated form of the corrugation can be clearly seen in the cut-away view. In this instance we have a stressed skin construction where the structure performs the whole duty of space enclosure leaving only the two ends to be filled in. The construction of a larger hangar of this type, having a span of more than 400 feet, was begun in Seville, but building seems to have been interrupted by the civil war.

Fig. 136, above, the roof of an exhibition hall 315 ft. wide at Turin, Italy is a continuous corrugated arch with longitudinal stiffening fins constructed of pre-cast concrete trough-shaped units assembled by means of reinforced concrete ribs poured in place along the crowns and hollows of the corrugations. (Architect: R. Biscaretti di Ruffia. Engineer: Pier Luigi Nervi.)

The same principle of construction, which makes the most efficient use of concrete in compression, was used in an Exhibition Hall at Turin, Italy (fig. 136) but in this case the continuous corrugated arch is brought down on to point supports in a rather remarkable way. Owing to the short time available for the construction of this building, an interesting system was adopted using pre-cast units assembled by field-poured-concrete. The main part of the roof consists entirely of pre-cast trough-shaped elements, with stiffening fins to keep their shape and openings for light on either side; they were erected on tubular formwork and assembled into a monolithic structure by means of reinforced concrete ribs poured in place along the crowns and hollows of the corrugations. The total span of this roof at the base of its supporting buttresses is 315 feet and the depth of the corrugation at the crown, about 61 feet above the floor, is over 5 feet.

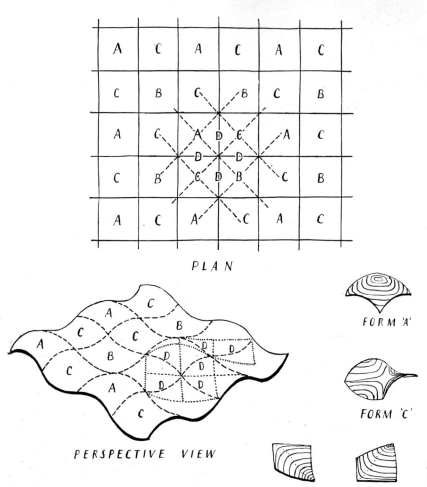

PLAN

PERSPECTIVE VIEW

FORM 'A'

FORM 'C'

FORM 'D'

Fig. 137, left, basic types of shell curved in two directions as derived from a typical doubly corrugated surface.

Shells of double curvature

The last two examples make use of corrugations of an angular type where the sides of the corrugations are formed of straight lines. Pursuing the principles of curved forms, however, as seen in the arch rib and the barrel vault shell, we should expect a curved corrugation to be the more efficient structural form, since angles result in bending stresses. Also in the last two illustrations the width of the corrugations is small compared with the span of the single arch curve of the roof structure. It is therefore interesting to study the general case of a surface with double curved corrugations of equal radii to see what forms can be developed from it. Fig. 137 shows a plan and perspective view of a shell or surface of this kind, from which it can be seen that it is composed of alternating squares, of domes (A), inverted domes (B), and saddle shapes (C), the latter having their centres in the same plane as their corners. Alternatively, the area can be divided diagonally as shown on the plan, producing a series of shapes (D) in which the four corners do not all lie in the same plane. This shape, in the same way as the dome, has two versions, one in which the fourth corner is above the other three, and one in which it is below them. The contours of types A, C and D are shown in separate sketches to illustrate their form. Type B is a surface which if used structurally would be entirely in tension, rather like a tarpaulin suspended from four corners, and is the shell equivalent of a suspension bridge cable. Types C and D, as used in practice, are known as hyperbolic paraboloids and the structural use of these forms seems to have been developed initially in France where the first example was constructed less than twenty years ago. More recently the use of these shells curved in two directions, has been adopted in Czechoslovakia where large factory areas have been covered in this way, with shells not more than 2½ inches thick.

Fig. 138, left, flexible jute fabric draped over steel arch ribs provides a simple formwork for pouring a thin arched concrete shell of corrugated section. (Engineers: Barchild Constructions, Ltd.)

Fig. 139, right, construction of a large store building at Umtali, South Rhodesia, using the system shown in Fig. 138. The shell, which in this case is reinforced, is 2½ inches thick and the span between internal lattice girder frames is 35 ft. (Engineers: Barchild Constructions, Ltd.)

Most examples of the saddle-type so far constructed seem to have the radius of the curve in one direction large compared with that in the other, owing to the way in which they are used. What is perhaps the simplest form of the double curved shell, is of much the same conception as the hangars at Orly. It makes use of a flexible jute fabric draped over temporary steel arch formwork (fig. 138), which produces a natural corrugated section on which is poured a thin layer of concrete. For smaller spans it can be used with no reinforcement but the jute fabric on which the concrete is poured. This system has been used for quite a number of structures in England, Eire and elsewhere for spans up to 60 feet, and one example is shown in fig. 139. This is a large store building at Umtali, Southern Rhodesia which uses a series of these corrugated arches 2½ inches thick, and in this case reinforced, spanning 35 feet between internal frames of columns and lattice girders; the outside bays which terminate in the complete arch form have a span of 47 feet. This has apparently been developed further, and in later construction of this type, the shell itself is made to span between supporting columns and the lattice girders are therefore eliminated.

Double-curved elements of entirely new form

117

This method of constructing the shell, forms an irregular corrugation in which the radius of the troughs is large compared with that of the crowns where the draped formwork passes over its supports. The resulting form is virtually a series of narrow saddle shapes (see fig. 137 'C') side by side, in which the arched span of the saddle is large compared with the width of its upward concave curve. It is a form which has been developed for single spans in Czechoslovakia, having a comparatively small rise and with ties to resist lateral thrust. Fig. 140 shows a factory store-house having three separate spans constructed in this manner, each of about 66 ft. The main and sag ties are placed at the junctions of the saddle shapes over the columns. In the example shown, the three spans are arranged so as to provide clerestory lighting but there is no reason why direct lighting should not be obtained in the shell roof itself. This can be done by separating the saddle elements into self-contained structural units suitably stiffened at the edges. They may be arranged in groups, or completely separated with a space for lighting in between each shell, as seen in a tannery also in Czechoslovakia (fig. 141). In this case the span is 90 feet and the ties are placed under the space between the saddle shells, where the columns occur. Both these examples are in reinforced concrete constructed with normal timber formwork. In France the same form as the latter structure was carried out in steel in the construction of a hangar having a span of nearly 250 feet. The steel saddle shells were stiffened by lattice ribs on the underside and were carried down in the complete arch form on to concrete buttresses. Glazing was arranged as in the last example by leaving a space in between each shell equal to its own width of about 14 feet.

Fig. 140, above, left and right, a factory storehouse in Czechoslovakia has three spans of about 66 ft. roofed with a continuous saddle type of hyperbolic paraboloid concrete shell tied internally. The heights are arranged to give clerestory lighting in the centre bay. (Engineer: Konrad Hruban.)

Fig. 141 left and above, a tannery in Czechoslovakia having a roof of 90 ft. span composed of hyperbolic paraboloid concrete shells of saddle shape spaced apart to provide continuous glazed areas at regular intervals. (Engineer: Konrad Hruban.)

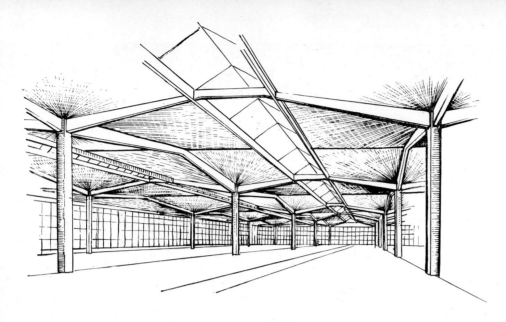

Fig. 142, left, interior view of a factory in Czechoslovakia which has a roof of a series of hyperbolic paraboloid shell concrete elements in each of which one corner is below the plane of the other three.

Fig. 143, above, left and right, hangars at Luneberg, Germany are roofed with barrels of corrugated steel plate, arched into bowstring form by means of rolled steel joist ties. (Photo: British Crown Copyright Reserved.)

The type of shell with one corner above or below the plane of the other three, (see fig. 137 'D'), seems to be most useful in cases where hips or valleys would normally be required, providing shell forms of comparatively small rise suitable for the roofing of areas which are approximately square on plan. Most examples of this type appear to have been carried out in France, but this form, also, seems to be receiving attention in Czechoslovakia and one application is shown in fig. 142 which makes use of four shells of this type in each bay.

The forms of double-curved shell so far considered, owe their existence entirely to modern structural materials, in contrast to the dome which has been constructed for so long out of small non-tensile units. What modern materials have done for the dome, however, is to eliminate the necessity for massive abutment and continuous support, as well as reducing the dome thickness and making possible the construction of a multitude of shapes, curved in two directions but not true rotational domes.

Fig. 144, above, left and right, shell concrete domes, square on plan and supported on columns, are used to cover areas 90 ft. x 70 ft. in a factory for Enfield Cables, Ltd. at Brynmawr, South Wales. The edges are stiffened with lattice girders, which provide clerestory lighting to supplement the light obtained through the circular apertures in the domes. (Architects: Architects' Co-operative Partnership. Engineers: Ove Arup and Partners.)

The latter point is well illustrated by the example shown in fig. 143 which would scarcely be regarded as a dome although it is curved in two directions. Its main characteristic is that the radius of the curve in one direction is small compared with that in the other and it therefore represents the general case of a structural form of which the true rotational dome is a particular example when the two curves are of equal radius. The structure illustrated is one of a number of hangars of the same type constructed in Germany during World War II. It consists of a series of barrel shells made of steel plate about ⅛″ thick, itself corrugated in cross-section to increase the stiffness (see foreground in fig. 143), and tied into arched shape in the direction of the span by means of steel joists. The arched shape of the barrel shell itself, is maintained by internal lattice bracing as can be seen in the interior view. This system has apparently been used for spans up to 300 feet and it is said to have been developed further, so as to dispense with the horizontal ties. A double curved shell which is more recognisable as a dome is shown in fig. 144 and this example also illustrates the fact that the shell dome can be carried on point supports. The building illustrated is a factory at Brynmawr in South Wales, the main part of which is roofed with nine domes each covering a rectangular bay measuring 90 feet by 70 feet and having a thickness of 3 inches over most of their surface. The dome is stiffened and held in shape by means of lattice girders along all four edges, which provide clerestory lighting to supplement the light obtained through the circular apertures in the dome surface. Square domes of this type have apparently been constructed with a considerably greater span and it is thought that even with a span of 300 feet it should be possible to construct a dome having a thickness of not more than 4 inches.[17]

[17]See H. G. Cousins—reference above.

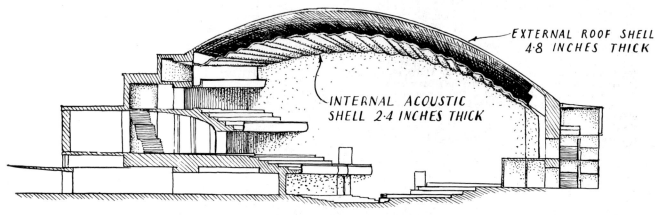

EXTERNAL ROOF SHELL
4·8 INCHES THICK

INTERNAL ACOUSTIC
SHELL 2·4 INCHES THICK

LONGITUDINAL SECTION

Fig. 145, above and right, the concert hall
in the Broadcasting Center at Copenhagen,
Denmark, is roofed with two doubly curved
concrete shells, the outer one 4¾ inches
thick, the inner one 2½ inches thick and
undulated for acoustic purposes. (Architect:
Vilhelm Lauritzen.)

**Double-curved
shells of
irregular shape**

At the same time, the double-curved shell is not limited to the regular shapes so far illustrated and one of its big advantages is that it makes possible the roofing of an irregularly shaped area with a single structural element, so that curved roofing forms are no longer limited to areas which are circular, square, or rectangular on plan. Fig. 145 shows the roof of the Broadcasting Center in Copenhagen which is a typical example of the way in which the shell can be adapted to the requirements of contemporary architectural problems. This roof is constructed of two doubly-curved concrete shells, an outer one which has a thickness of 4¾ inches and an inner one 2½ inches thick which is undulated according to the required acoustic profile. The stress analysis of such irregular shells, however, is extremely complicated and in this instance, for example, the calculations are said to have occupied a team of four engineers for more than six months.[18]

[18]See Ove N. Arup "Shell construction" in Architectural Design (England), November, 1947.

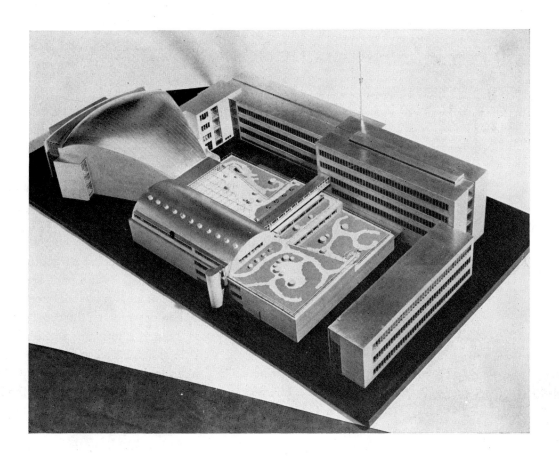

Fig. 146, above, elliptical concrete shell domes of 150 ft. diameter perform the entire duty of space enclosure at the Sewage Treatment Plant, Hibbing, Minnesota. (Architect: J. C. Taylor. Engineers: C. Foster; Roberts and Schaefer Co.)

The complete space-enclosing shell

The shell dome carried on columns retains, in the same way as the barrel vault shell, the advantages associated with point supports. The elliptical shells illustrated in fig. 146, represent the final development where the load is transferred by means of the shell itself and the monolithic structure performs the entire duty of space enclosure above the ground. These reinforced concrete domes, of 150 ft. span and minimum thickness of 3½ inches, are trickling filters of a sewage treatment plant at Hibbing, Minnesota. It is in the Horton-spheroid fuel tanks in Southern Texas, however, as seen in fig. 147, that the complete three-dimensional stressed skin appears, rising out of the ground as an entire space enclosing structural element and therefore no longer dependent on the ground itself as the final space enclosing plane. These fuel tanks are constructed of welded steel plate stiffened internally and have a span of 127 feet. A canteen for the men engaged on the construction of these reservoirs was built on the same system, having a total span of about 94 feet. That the use of the spherical stressed skin as a combined structural and space-enclosing element provides new scope in design, is demonstrated in the project for a concert hall shown in fig. 148, where a form very much akin to that of the Horton-spheroids results from the complete integration of the structure with the requirements of vision and acoustics.

Fig. 147, above, shell construction in stiffened welded sheet steel of the 127 ft. diameter Horton-spheroid fuel tanks (80,000 bbl.) in southern Texas, provides a complete three-dimensional space-enclosing structure.

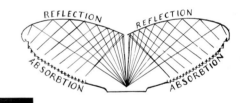

SECTION

Fig. 148, left and above, project for a concert hall in which the structural shape, developed from requirements of vision and acoustics, takes on a form very much akin to that of the Horton-spheroids. (Architect: Amancio Williams.)

II.

Structure in Architectural Design

The divorce of engineer and architect in the nineteenth century displaced structure from its traditional place in architectural evolution, and it is only in recent years that pioneer work has shown the way in which contemporary structural development can form the basis of a new and vigorous architecture.

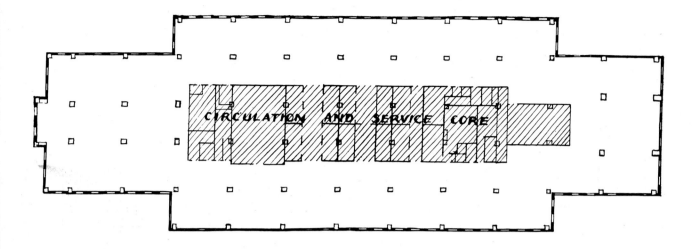

DIAGRAMMATIC FLOOR PLAN

Fig. 149, left and above, the 850 ft. high R.C.A. Building in Rockefeller Center, New York, with 70 floors of offices, shows the large proportion of plan occupied by the circulation core, where good natural lighting is required for the whole working area. (Architects: Reinhard and Hofmeister; Corbett, Harrison and Macmurray; and Hood and Fouilhoux.)

Plan

Whilst the plan and its economy is largely influenced by the height of a building and the nature of its materials, the ability to construct multi-storey buildings increases the importance of vertical circulation to such an extent, that it becomes more influential in its architectural significance than the actual bulk of the structure. Fig. 149 shows the 850 ft. high R.C.A. building in Rockefeller Center, New York, with 70 floors of offices, illustrating the large area occupied by the circulation and service core. The dimensions of each floor are determined by the provision of adequate natural lighting to the whole of the working area. With this requirement as a governing factor, increasing the height of a building merely increases the proportion of plan occupied by the circulation core, and it is therefore not surprising to find that although the economical height depends very much on current land values, there seems to be a limit beyond which a sharp decline in the economic return seems to call a halt.[19] It appears therefore, that the necessity for vertical circulation is likely to limit the proportions of the skyscraper slab form as an architectural element arising out of contemporary structure.

Structure and plan economy

[19]See "The Skyscraper" (A study in the economic height of modern office buildings) by W. C. Clark and J. L. Kingston (American Institute of Steel Construction).

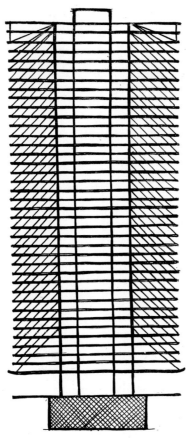

CROSS-SECTION of COMPLETE STRUCTURE

DETAIL of TYPICAL TRUSSED CANTILEVER

Fig. 150, above, project for a steel tension-structure of trussed cantilevers supported on central stanchions, making the maximum use of steel in pure tension and concentrating the compression stresses of load transfer in a few flexurally rigid members. (Architect: Guido Fiorini.)

Considerations in load transfer

The question of load transfer can be resolved into two processes—the provision of adequate material to sustain the loads and its disposition in such a way as to provide maximum structural economy and conformity with planning requirements. The distribution of material, however, affects the amount required, for the smaller the cross-section of each column for a given height, the more the permissible stress is likely to be reduced to allow for the tendency of slender members to buckle when under compression. It has been suggested that the conventional use of steel in multi-storey construction is not necessarily the most economical, since the most efficient use of the material is in pure tension where considerations of flexural rigidity are eliminated. This implies the concentration of compression stresses in a few members only which by reason of their cross-section and shape can be made to develop greater strength. Fig. 150 shows a proposal for such a scheme which is claimed to provide a lighter structure as well as a series of standard floor plans. Apart from the central core, the whole of the building is free from the weight of floors above, so that two thirds of the structure consists of repetitive elements, providing considerable economy and the possibility of using standardised constructional units at each floor. In conventional frames there is an increase in weight per

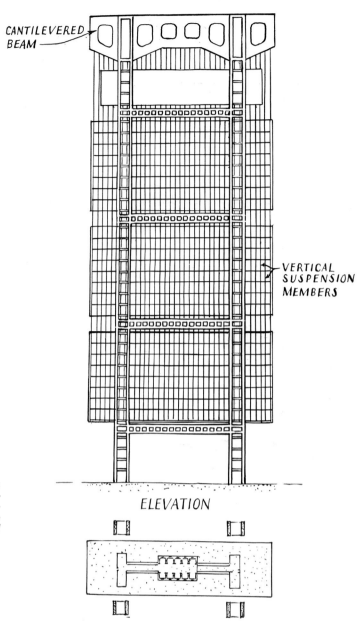

CANTILEVERED BEAM

VERTICAL SUSPENSION MEMBERS

ELEVATION

TYPICAL PLAN

Fig. 151, right, project for a suspension frame office building, in which four massive columns support deep overhead cantilevered beams from which all floors are suspended by means of continuous vertical hangers. (Architect: Amancio Williams.)

cubic foot in proportion to the height of the building, but this factor is claimed to be almost eliminated in this system.[20] The encasement of the steelwork in concrete, for protection against fire and corrosion, obviously diminishes the advantage of a tension member, but since the compressive value of the concrete encasement in a steel compression member is not normally utilised to any great extent (see Appendix), the tension member still remains more efficient particularly if made of high tensile steel. Moreover, new methods of protection such as spraying with asbestos or vermiculite, may completely change this aspect of the problem. The system just described virtually makes use of a series of trussed cantilevers and this is obviously limited in its application. An alternative method of employing tension members is to use deep cantilevered beams at the top of the building with vertical hangers to carry the ends of all beams. A project based on this principle is shown in fig. 151 where the load of the whole building is concentrated in four massive columns.[21]

[20]See "Tension-structure" in Bollettino Tecnico Savigliano (Italy) April, 1932.

[21]See "Edificio Para Oficinas" in Revista de Arquitectura (Argentine), May, 1948.

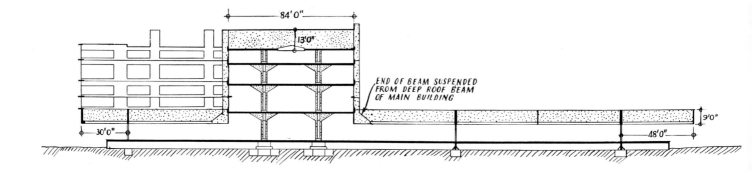

84' 0"

13' 0"

END OF BEAM SUSPENDED
FROM DEEP ROOF BEAM
OF MAIN BUILDING

30' 0"

48' 0"

9' 0"

CROSS SECTION

Fig. 152, above and below, factory extension for Messrs. Boots Pure Drug Co. at
Beeston, England, in which the ends of the
multi-storey floors and the single-storey
roof are supported on hangers suspended
from deep cantilevered beams above the
roof, to provide a clear ground floor area
below. (Architect and Engineer: Sir E. Owen
Williams.)

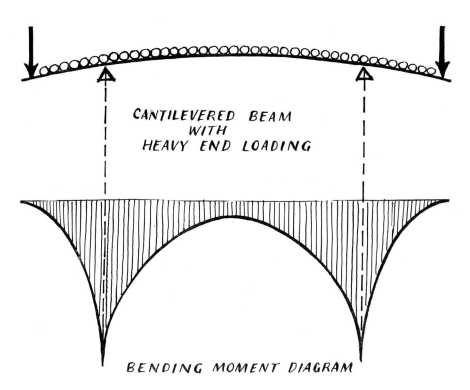

CANTILEVERED BEAM
WITH
HEAVY END LOADING

BENDING MOMENT DIAGRAM

Fig. 153, above, a heavily end-loaded cantilevered beam may be entirely in negative bending and if placed above the roof of a building can make use of the roof slab as a compression flange.

A tension structure can clearly provide the advantage of minimum obstruction of the circulating plane at ground level, together with an unrestricted outer perimeter in the ground floor plan. A special case involving these requirements was the extension to the factory at Beeston, England (fig. 152), where it was desired to eliminate columns at the junction of the multi-storey and single-storey buildings. The structure in this case is of reinforced concrete, having deep cantilevered beams above the roof; these support tension members which pick up the loads from the ends of the multi-storey floors and the single-storey roof. In a case like this, with heavy loads on the ends of the cantilevers, the cantilevered beam is likely to be entirely in negative bending (fig. 153) and the roof slab forms a convenient compression flange, suitable for composite construction (see Appendix) as well as for reinforced concrete. In the long run, the economy of such systems must obviously depend upon a balance between the saving of material in vertical members, and the probable increased cost of the rest of the structure.

Integration of plan and structure

Because the multi-storey structure was the outcome of the introduction of steel in an essentially linear form, it has been slow to move beyond the conception of a complete skeleton frame. The result is that multi-storey buildings are mostly found to be burdened with vast quantities of inactive material performing the functions of space enclosure but playing the part of a passenger in the structural vehicle. It would seem, therefore, that progress in structural economy might be usefully sought in the harnessing to structural duties of more of the building fabric, through the greater integration of structure into architectural design. The plans of most multi-storey buildings demonstrate certain definite features in common. The circulation core of elevator shafts and staircases; vertical service ducts; cloakrooms of office blocks; bathrooms and kitchens of apartments; all these are essentially permanent features in view of the mechanical installations which go into them or the particular forms which they are given. The 'free plan' introduced by the skeleton frame undoubtedly had its value in the Tugendhat house (fig. 154) but in multi-storey construction is often unnecessary and may not be structurally, or even architecturally, the best solution to the problems involved. Instead, these permanent features provide the opportunity for the spreading out of the structural material to enclose them, forming hollow structural members which, by virtue of their great inherent rigidity, offer the maximum efficiency in compression. Although reinforced concrete is perhaps the most suitable material for structural units of this kind, the use of suitably stiffened steel has also been suggested (see Appendix).

An approach to these principles is to be found in a research building in San Francisco (fig. 155). The form of this is still that of a complete skeleton frame, but advantage has been taken of the two central circulation and service cores, to introduce concrete walls as bracing elements against wind and earthquake forces, thus uniting groups of four columns into rigid structural units. The ultimate development is demonstrated in a Laboratory Tower at Racine, Wisconsin (fig. 156). Here the use of the central supporting core has been combined with the great inherent strength of the complete circle in the mushroom form, referred to in the previous chapter. The central core enclosing circulation and services, has a diameter of about fifteen feet, and each floor spreads out about the same distance beyond it. The building is square in shape, however, and the corner portions of floor slab are suspended from spandrel cantilevers supported on the perimeters of the mushrooms. This is emphasised by the retention of the circular plan at alternate floors. In order to provide stability, the central core of this fifteen storey building has been carried down very deep into the ground to form an anchorage. Even if it is thought extravagant, this structure is of great architectural significance, since it shows the multi-storey building in a form as far removed from the skeleton frame as the latter was from the load-bearing wall. It points the way to a new conception in multi-storey construction, based upon greater integration of structure and plan. Noise transmission might be an objection to the use of stair or elevator shafts as structural members, but the tendency towards designing stair and elevator supports as independent structures (see fig. 101), seems to provide the possibility of combining a structural enclosure isolated from both staircase and elevator.

Fig. 154, above, the 'free plan' of the Tugendhat house at Brno, Czechoslovakia, is often not required in multi-storey construction. (Architect: Ludwig Mies van der Rohe.)

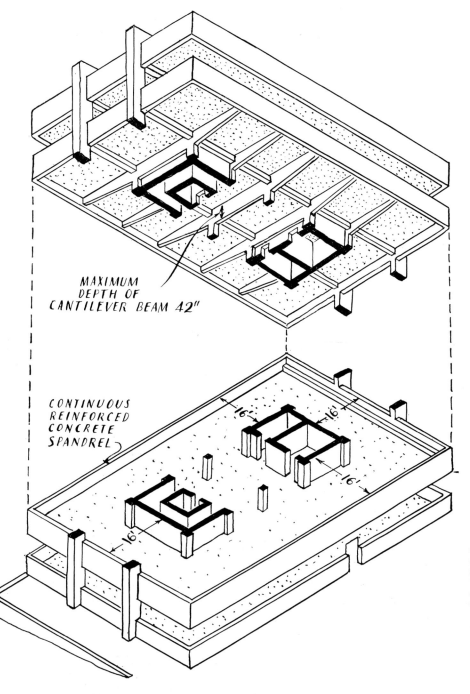

MAXIMUM DEPTH OF CANTILEVER BEAM 42"

CONTINUOUS REINFORCED CONCRETE SPANDREL

Fig. 155, left, the Ruth Lucie Stern Research Building, San Francisco, in which groups of the two lines of columns from which all floors are cantilevered, are united into rigid structural elements to enclose circulation and service cores and at the same time to resist lateral forces. (Architects: Birge M. Clark and David B. Clark.)

Although the principle of concentration of support could probably be combined with the use of more conventional framing members, insufficient repetition, when used alone, may make the former uneconomical, and such systems can therefore only be regarded as supplementing the normal skeleton frame. It has been usual to design the latter on as uniform a grid as possible, to provide the maximum economy within the limitations of a nominally pin-jointed frame, but the trend towards monolithic construction, bringing greater attention to bear on the balance of forces within the structure, suggests a different approach to this matter. For instance bays of unequal span may, in some cases, provide greater equalisation of moments in continuous members. The latter require cantilevered end bays for maximum efficiency, to provide negative moments over the end supports, and these in turn produce greater equalisation of column loads and a reduction of eccentric loading on the outside columns; this is particularly important in the case of the flat slab diaphragm. Thus, whilst the eccentrically loaded external column and bays of equal span are characteristic of a pin-jointed frame, structural economy introduced by rigid frames produces cantilevered end bays and possibly intermediate bays of unequal span. The extent to which the resulting column spacing affects planning requirements, must obviously depend upon the degree of interdependence between structure and plan.

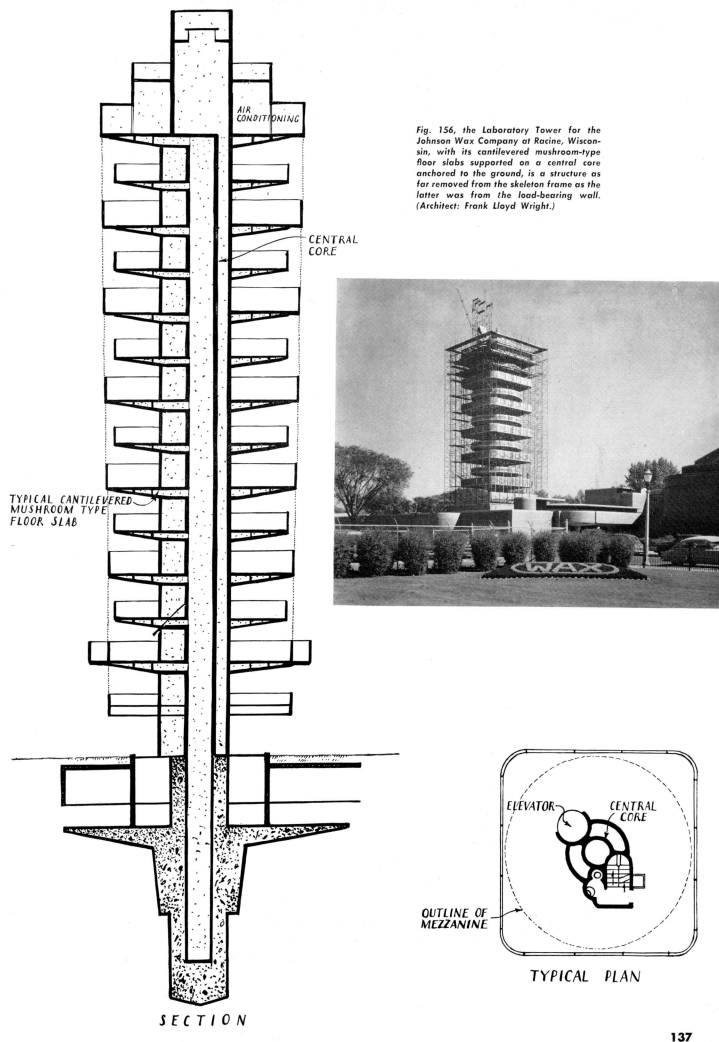

AIR
CONDITIONING

CENTRAL
CORE

TYPICAL CANTILEVERED
MUSHROOM TYPE
FLOOR SLAB

SECTION

Fig. 156, the Laboratory Tower for the
Johnson Wax Company at Racine, Wisconsin, with its cantilevered mushroom-type
floor slabs supported on a central core
anchored to the ground, is a structure as
far removed from the skeleton frame as the
latter was from the load-bearing wall.
(Architect: Frank Lloyd Wright.)

ELEVATOR   CENTRAL
                CORE

OUTLINE OF
MEZZANINE

TYPICAL PLAN

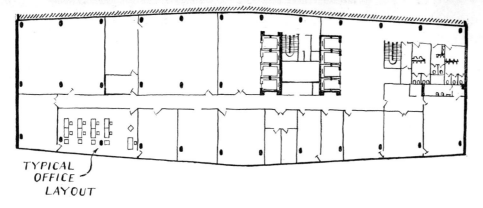

TYPICAL
OFFICE
LAYOUT

Fig. 157, above, typical floor plan of the office building for the Rio Grande Do Sul Railway, Porto Alegre, Brazil, shows how free-standing columns resulting from canti-levered end bays can be of aesthetic value in large office units. (Architects: Alfonso E. Reidy and Jorge M. Moreira.)

Fig. 158, right, mushroom columns in the Administration Building of the Johnson Wax Company, Racine, Wisconsin, help to humanise the scale by providing focal points which break down a large and lofty area. (Architect: Frank Lloyd Wright.)

Basic plan types

The three basic types of problem are, the open floor area as required in trade or industry, the floor area requiring divisions of a temporary and flexible nature as in office buildings, and that requiring permanent divisions as in flats, hotels etc. Cantilevered external bays are particularly suited to the first type where no divisions occur and unobstructed light is normally an asset, but their use with the other types is more dependent on the degree to which the columns must be incorporated into walls and partitions. The comparatively large units of office requirements and the nature of the temporary partitions, seem to provide suitable conditions for use of the free-standing column. This principle is illustrated in the typical floor plan of an office building designed for erection in Porto Alegre, Brazil (fig. 157). To an office, which may be bare and impersonal, the free-standing column of suitable shape may well be of aesthetic value; this is illustrated on an unusually large scale in the Administration Building at Racine, Wisconsin (fig. 158), where the columns undoubtedly provide focal points which contribute towards the breaking down of the lofty area and the humanising of the scale. On the other hand, the free-standing column does not seem to have a wide application in the smaller spatial units of the domestic field, except perhaps in living areas, entries, or those rooms in which built-in furniture and fitments predominate.

The free-standing column

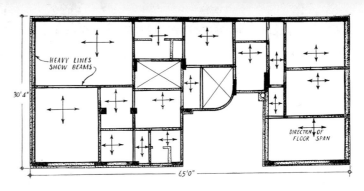

Fig. 159, right, typical floor plan of a sixteen storey apartment block in Rio de Janeiro, Brazil, shows how the reinforced concrete frame has been moulded to suit the exigencies of the plan and the thickness of walls and partitions.

PLAN (Looking Up)

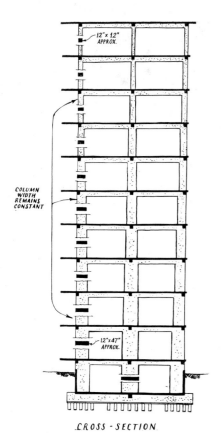

CROSS - SECTION

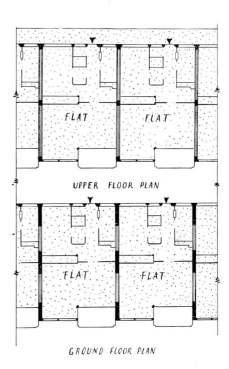

UPPER FLOOR PLAN

Fig. 160, left and right, simplified units in the Plaslaan apartment building in Rotterdam, Holland, provide an economical method of absorbing the cross frames in the division walls by keeping all columns to a constant width. (Architects: W. van Tijen and H. A. Maaskant.)

GROUND FLOOR PLAN

Structure moulded to suit the plan

The alternative, of incorporating the structure into walls and partitions, has recently been receiving greater attention, with the object of eliminating undesirable projections of beams and columns. In a sixteen storey apartment block in Rio de Janeiro, of which the typical plan is shown in fig. 159, the reinforced concrete frame has been moulded to suit the plan in such a way that the only evidence of the structure is to be found in the kitchen and bathroom. All beams are of a standard depth and of such a width as not to project outside partitions or external walls. On the other hand, the general framing pattern in this case produces numerous beams bearing on other beams, and maximum structural economy clearly requires simplification of the planning units. This was done in an apartment building at Rotterdam, Holland (fig. 160), where the dwelling units are contained between simple cross frames in which columns are kept to a constant width and therefore become very deep in the lower storeys; this is not only economical in form-work, but also provides increased resistance to wind-pressure. By using a double partition between apartments, where it is required for sound insulation, the structure becomes absorbed into the division walls leaving only cross beams to be integrated with the plan of the dwelling unit. The trend towards the box wall is immediately apparent in the lower part of these frames.

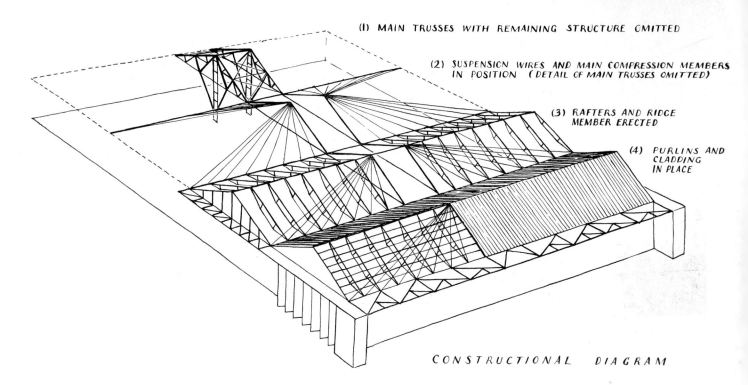

(1) MAIN TRUSSES WITH REMAINING STRUCTURE OMITTED

(2) SUSPENSION WIRES AND MAIN COMPRESSION MEMBERS IN POSITION (DETAIL OF MAIN TRUSSES OMITTED)

(3) RAFTERS AND RIDGE MEMBER ERECTED

(4) PURLINS AND CLADDING IN PLACE

CONSTRUCTIONAL DIAGRAM

Fig. 161, above and left, projected hangar design for British European Airways employs a modified type of shell design in steel to produce a double cantilever roof on central supports, providing areas of 100 ft. depth with unobstructed outer perimeters. (Architect: Christopher Nicholson. Engineer: F. J. Samuely.)

The cellular plan

From a planning point of view, the box wall is most suited to the type of building which can be broken down into self-contained cells, making it particularly useful for domestic work. Since the floor slabs provide sufficient stiffness without tie beams, intermediate frames like the ones in the Rotterdam building can be introduced to increase the scope of the unit, without impairing the clean lines of the structure. Box wall construction provides a very clear statement of the fact that contemporary society requires the super-imposing of self-contained units, which in former times would have been constructed side by side, and it can contribute very greatly towards the use of more of the building fabric in a structural role. At the same time, since the structural slab of the box frame can be regarded as a beam as well as a column, it can be picked up by point supports or receive point loads, permitting a greater flexibility in the superimposing of plans of differing types.

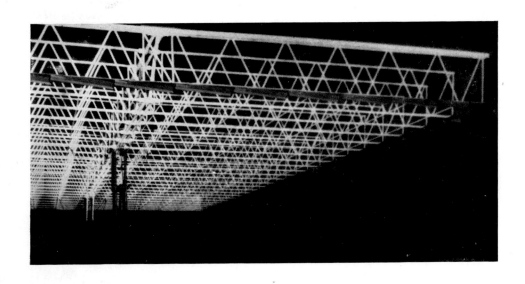

Fig. 162, above, right, and below, project for an airplane hangar constructed of cantilevered girders built out of standardized tubular steel members has four central supports with unobstructed access on all sides. (Architect: Konrad Wachsmann. Engineer: Paul Weidlinger.)

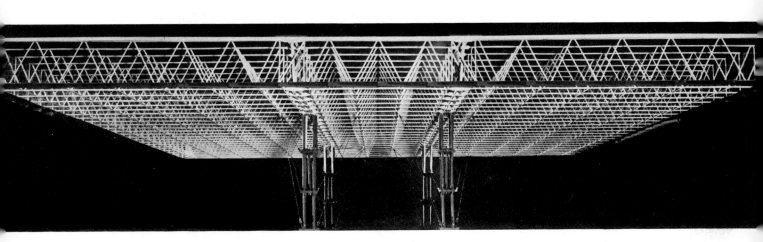

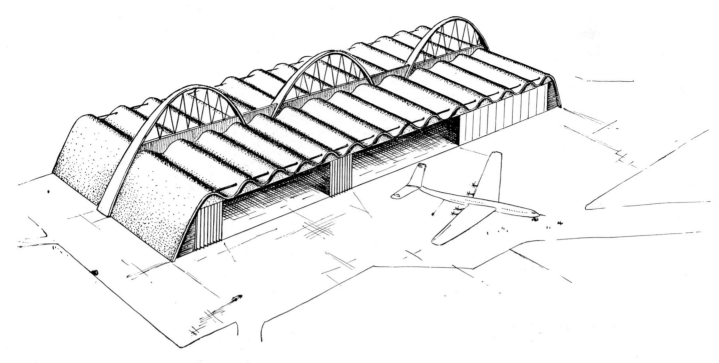

Fig. 163, above, project for an airplane hangar constructed of very large span arches with double cantilevered shells of corrugated section suspended from them, anticipates hangars of the future approaching the order of bridge construction. (Architect: Leonard Michaels.)

Structure in single-storey planning

In large span single-storey construction, although continuity of beams assumes great importance from a structural point of view, its full use may be restricted by clear span requirements which necessitate the incorporation of columns in the external walls. For most purposes, clear internal spans are the main criterion, but in airplane hangars it is found that the arrangement of the planes to face in alternate directions, which is the most economical method of housing them, requires an unobstructed outer perimeter as well as a clear internal area. There seems, therefore, to be a significant development towards the concentration of support at the centre of the building, resulting in double cantilevered roofs. The design shown in fig. 161, uses a system of tension members similar to those of the multi-storey structure previously described, to provide cantilevers of 100 feet span either side of the supporting columns. In this case the tension members are arranged in the slope of the pitched roofs, with all the compression concentrated in members at the eaves. By this means areas 100 feet deep and of any required length could be obtained, with completely unobstructed access, and in this instance the proposed structure was to be 630 feet long. The use of reinforced concrete shell cantilevers for this type of hangar would seem to be very suitable and, in fact, the steel design described, is a compromise necessitated by the difficulties of fabricating a true shell in steel. A further proposal using tubular steel (fig. 162) provides completely centralised supports with unobstructed access on all sides, but the actual clear areas in this case are rather smaller, the whole structure measuring 140 feet by 200 feet. Since air transport of the future seems likely to demand structures of much greater dimensions, the next stage of structural development may well approach the order of bridge construction, with arches of very great span having, say, a double cantilevered shell roof suspended from them (fig. 163).

Fig. 164, right and below, detail of the Exhibition Hall at Turin, Italy shows the skillful way in which the corrugated stressed skin roof is canalized onto the point support arch ribs at about 25 ft. intervals in a manner reminiscent of Gothic vaulting. (Architect: R. Biscaretti di Ruffia. Engineer: Pier Luigi Nervi.)

In contrast to the point supports and free access of these systems, the stressed skin construction of the type used in the hangars at Orly (fig. 135), is inclined to be limited in its planning conception. Nevertheless, it presents a challenge to the skill and ingenuity of architects and structural designers in applying the new structural forms to planning requirements. This fact is well borne-out in the design of the Exhibition Hall at Turin (fig. 164) where the necessity of carrying a continuous corrugated stressed skin on point supports was met in a most skillful manner reminiscent of the finest essays in Gothic vaulting. At the same time, in the complete stressed skin enclosure such as the concert-hall project in fig. 148, the interdependence of plan and structure reaches the extreme limit previously only associated with load-bearing walls.

Plan and the stressed skin

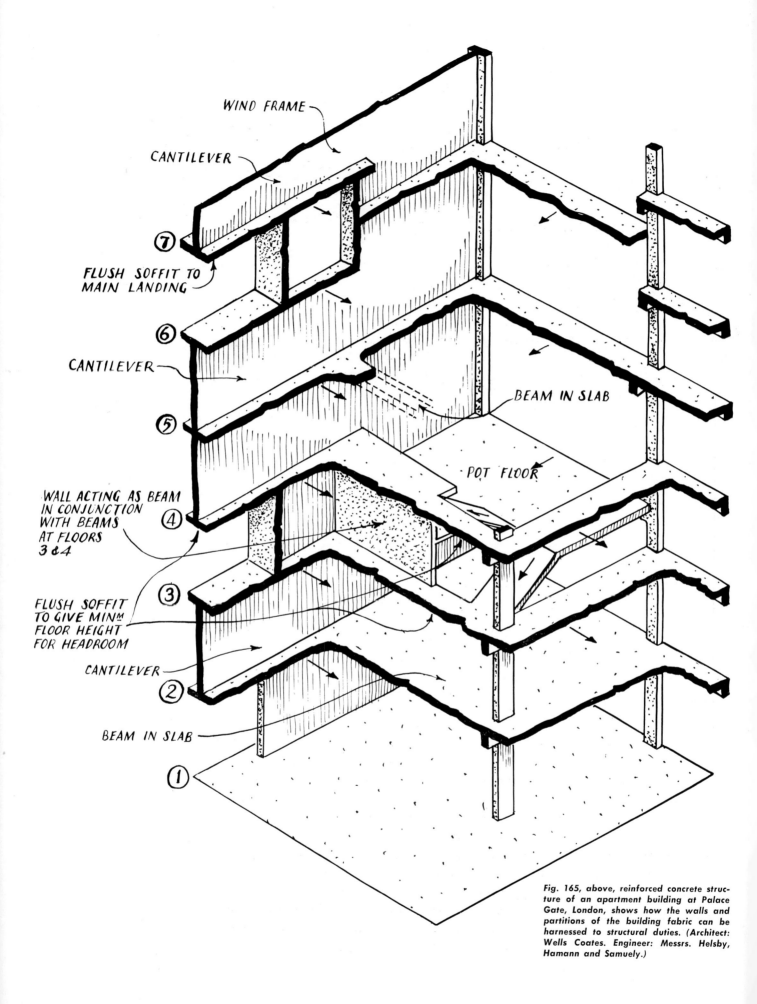

WIND FRAME

CANTILEVER

⑦

FLUSH SOFFIT TO
MAIN LANDING

⑥

CANTILEVER

⑤

BEAM IN SLAB

POT FLOOR

WALL ACTING AS BEAM
IN CONJUNCTION
WITH BEAMS
AT FLOORS
3 & 4

④

FLUSH SOFFIT
TO GIVE MINᵐ
FLOOR HEIGHT
FOR HEADROOM

③

CANTILEVER

②

BEAM IN SLAB

①

Fig. 165, above, reinforced concrete structure of an apartment building at Palace
Gate, London, shows how the walls and
partitions of the building fabric can be
harnessed to structural duties. (Architect:
Wells Coates. Engineer: Messrs. Helsby,
Hamann and Samuely.)

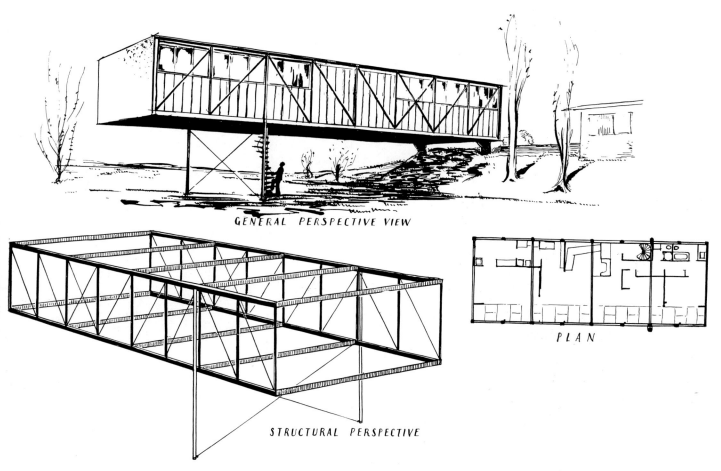

GENERAL PERSPECTIVE VIEW

STRUCTURAL PERSPECTIVE

PLAN

Fig. 166, above, a small house, which, in order to exploit the site conditions, is conceived as a lattice steel box beam cantilevered out over two steel supports. (Architects: Charles Eames and Eero Saarinen.)

Section

Section is related to plan mainly through the medium of structure. Continuity and pre-stressing contribute towards higher span/depth ratios and reinforced concrete permits the use of deep narrow beams which can be assimilated into walls and partitions; the Vierendeel truss results from intercommunication and the provision of light and air. These structural developments indicate the amount of inactive material which the section of a normal multi-storey building might reveal. By breathing life into more of this inert matter, we may find not only structural economy, but also greater flexibility in design, as shown in an apartment building in London (fig. 165), where dividing walls are used also as beams and cantilevers. A counterpart in steel-work is shown in fig. 166, where site conditions have been exploited to provide a simple but interesting design for a small house, by conceiving the whole unit as a box beam cantilevered out over two steel supports.

DOUBLE CONCRETE FLOOR
WITH HOLLOW TILE INFILLING

CHANNEL SHAPED
SPANDREL BEAM IS
USED AS A SERVICE
DUCT. ACCESS IS
PROVIDED BY REMOV-
ABLE FACING OF
GLASS PANELS IN
TEAK·FRAMING

HINGED MULLIONS
TAKE ONLY DIRECT STRESSES
WIND STRESS IS TAKEN BY
SOLID END WALLS

SECTIONAL VIEW

Fig. 167, Finsbury Health Centre, London, in which the whole spandrel becomes a beam of channel shape and a horizontal duct, supported on closely spaced hinged mullions. The parapet over the entrance hall becomes a beam of fairly long span. (Architects: Tecton. Engineers: Messrs. J. L. Kier and Co., Ltd.)

A closer integration of structure and section, in the same way as shown for the plan, seems likely to create a more efficient use of materials and a closer approach to architectural requirements. The parapet and spandrel become beams at Finsbury Health Centre, London, (fig. 167); the clerestorey is brought to life in a church at Eltham, England (fig. 168). Although depth in external walls is usually available for exploitation in this manner, for beams spanning across a building the choice normally lies between a medium span providing the necessary head room at each floor, or the use of a whole storey height as for instance in the Dorchester Hotel, London, where a reinforced concrete beam two storeys deep, spans a distance of fifty feet. Large spans or exceptionally heavy loading in multi-storey construction, therefore, present the problem of devoting at least every other storey to construc-

Integration of section and structure

Fig. 168, left and right, a church at Eltham, England, in which the clerestory becomes a lattice girder to free the floor space below. (Architect: J. O'Hanlon Hughes. Engineers: Holst and Co., Ltd.)

tional members, with consequent restrictions on their use; this is seen in a factory at Bristol, England (fig. 169) designed for very heavy loading where the 8 ft. high constructional floors are used for services and air conditioning required for the manufacturing process. One proposal adapts this feature to the requirements of a particular problem, the department store. By introducing intermediate stock floors to take up the required constructional depth, it is claimed that the general efficiency of the store is improved, to add to the advantage of unobstructed floor space (fig. 170). Construction of the columns on the slope, as shown in the section, increases the negative moments at the supports provided by the cantilevered ends of the trusses, and by this means it is stated that spans of over 200 feet could be achieved, with a constructional depth of only nine or ten feet.[22]

[22]See article by Dr. Louis Parnes in Architectural Record, February, 1947.

Fig. 169, below, heavily loaded beams in this factory for Messrs. Colodense, Ltd. at Bristol, England, occupy alternate storeys 8 ft. high which are used for services. (Architect: E. F. Peat. Engineer: F. J. Samuely.)

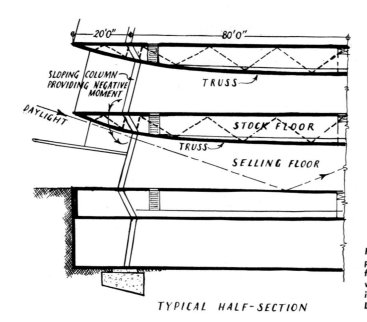

20'0"   80'0"

SLOPING COLUMN
PROVIDING NEGATIVE
MOMENT

TRUSS

DAYLIGHT

STOCK FLOOR

TRUSS

SELLING FLOOR

TYPICAL HALF-SECTION

Fig. 170, left and below, project for a department store employs intermediate stock floors to accommodate storey-height girders which are supported on sloping columns to increase the clear span. (Architect: Dr. Louis Parnes.)

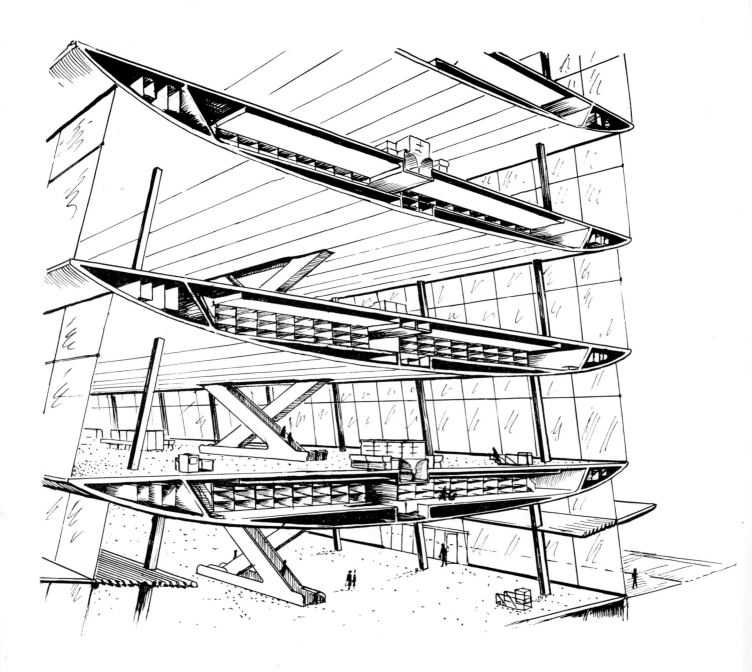

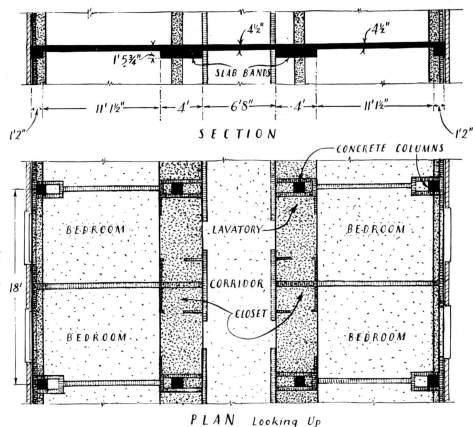

SECTION

CONCRETE COLUMNS

BEDROOM · · LAVATORY

CORRIDOR

CLOSET

BEDROOM

BEDROOM

BEDROOM

PLAN Looking Up

ig. 171, right, typical bay framing of Belle- ue Nurses Home, New York, shows how the slab-band can be made to follow those arts of the plan where reduced height be- omes an element of architectural design. Architects: Alfred Hopkins and Associates. ngineer: Fred N. Severud.)

Structural section and the plan

Since the disposition of beams will normally be reflected by the layout of columns, the relationship between columns and partitions must influence the section. The type of plan shown in fig. 157 with free-standing columns, requires either flat slab construction, a false ceiling, or some special type of double floor similar to that seen in fig. 167, if a clean appearance is to be provided; the false ceiling may clearly have advantages where extensive provision for services is required. Where the plan adheres to the structural grid, we have the example in the apartments at Rio de Janeiro, of beams being kept to a width of three to four inches, so as not to project beyond partitions; it should be noted, however, that under Brazilian regulations a smaller steel cover is required than in the U.S.A. and most other countries. The alternative to this method is to flatten out the beams into the slab-band form mentioned in the previous chapter, producing a structural arm which can be made to follow those parts of the plan where reduced heights are acceptable, such as corridors, cupboards, or vestibules to bedrooms. In a Nurses' Home in New York (fig. 171), where this system was employed, the slab-band is four feet wide; so that even where it cannot be arranged to come in such places as suggested, a band of such a width can be handled more satisfactorily than the conventional beam, by introducing a small reduction of height over some part of a room. The flattening out of beams in this manner can obviously provide a distinct advantage where head-room under beams is a critical factor. In the case of a large open plan, deep beams not only mean possible wasted pockets of space in each bay, but also inferior conditions of lighting and ventilation. The flat slab, therefore, seems to be the ideal form for this type of plan, since it can permit a saving of a foot or more in height from floor to floor, whilst providing better lighting conditions and improved ventilation due to the absence of air pockets; on the other hand there is less scope for the concealment of services.

Fig. 172, left, enclosure of the roof structure in the Exhibition Hall at Leipzig, Germany, provides a pleasant interior but this may not always be economical.

Fig. 173, right, the stressed skin provides clean flowing lines both internally and externally as seen in this saw-tooth shell roof of a factory for Messrs. Sotex, Ltd. at Congleton, England. (Architect: Rudolf Frankel. Engineers: Barrel Vault Roof (Designs) Ltd.)

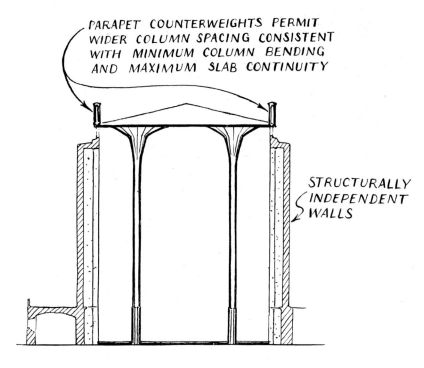

PARAPET COUNTERWEIGHTS PERMIT
WIDER COLUMN SPACING CONSISTENT
WITH MINIMUM COLUMN BENDING
AND MAXIMUM SLAB CONTINUITY

STRUCTURALLY
INDEPENDENT
WALLS

Fig. 174, right, project for a church in Poland demonstrates the structurally independent external wall arising out of the economical form of a continuous structure. (Architect: M. Nowicki.)

SECTION

The greater flexibility of design in the section of single-storey buildings is clearly due to the freedom of shape, which can combine structural depth with provision of natural lighting and the shedding of rainwater. The development whereby the roof plane becomes the active structural element, instead of being an inert infilling supported on an open framework, produces a tidying up of the structure, improving its appearance and permitting easier maintenance. Although enclosure of the framework internally, as in the Exhibition Hall at Leipzig (fig. 172), can provide a very pleasant interior, this is obviously uneconomical in many instances whereas the stressed skin roof provides of itself, clean lines internally as well as externally, as is well illustrated in a factory at Congleton, England (fig. 173). The flowing lines of this saw-tooth shell roof provide a very high standard of illumination over the whole working area due to the reflection from the curved surfaces and at the same time result in a far smoother flow of shapes externally than is obtainable with a conventional framed saw-tooth roof. The arch and rigid-frame promise to introduce similar improvements, whilst retaining the principle of frame and cladding. Buildings incorporating more particular functional requirements and where the stressed skin forms a complete enclosure, will reflect, even more strikingly, the close relationship between interior and exterior form. In the project for a concert-hall (fig. 148), the exterior form springs from a strict analysis of the internal acoustical problem related to the seating profile which is determined by the consideration of sight lines.

The economical form of a continuous structure means, in the case of a single-storey building, a structurally independent external wall as seen in the section of a proposed church in Poland (fig. 174); this may be emphasised by the use of continuous glazing at the junction of wall and roof, as seen both here and in the building at Racine (fig. 68). Alternatively, the balance of forces, a prime objective in structural economy, may produce a form such as that of the Empire Pool in London (fig. 65).

Fig. 175, above, left and right, projecting staircase tower of the Entertainments Pavilion, Bexhill, England, suspended from overhead cantilevers, portrays a new element in massing composition. (Architects: Eric Mendelsohn and Serge Chermayeff. Engineers: Messrs. Helsby, Hamann and Samuely.)

Massing

Massing, plan and the new materials

The interdependence of massing and structure clearly varies from a minimum with the skeleton frame, to a maximum in the case of the stressed skin enclosure. At the same time, the whole range of contemporary structure permits a greater flexibility between plan and massing, since loads can be collected with a greater degree of freedom. The former lack of tensile materials which created an aesthetic based upon the obvious relationship between load and support, made massing so dependent upon plan, that there was a natural tendency to split the essentially three-dimensional problem of space enclosure into two-dimensional problems of plan and section. With the development of the structural slab and shell, the influence of this conception is being replaced by a tendency towards freer three-dimensional composition.

Aesthetic of new mass relationships

The origin of the new aesthetic in which support is no longer grasped at sight, has been traced by Sigfried Giedion, to the projecting glass canopy used in France in the 1870's.[23] The freeing of the ground plan which is a characteristic of the tension structures previously illustrated, creates a mass which virtually hovers over the earth's surface. On a smaller scale, a feature introducing the principle of cantilever and suspension and creating a new element in massing composition, is the projecting staircase of the Pavilion at Bexhill, England; as seen in fig. 175, the whole structure is suspended from a pair of cantilevers at roof level, by means of vertical tension members which pick up the ends of the projecting landings. In pure skeleton construction, however, since it is the enclosing skin which provides the eventual

[23]See "Space, Time and Architecture" page 200.

Fig. 176, right, the suspended restaurant of the Co-operative Wholesale Society Offices, Stockholm, an element free in space, creates a new mass relationship between itself and adjacent buildings. (Architect: O. Thunstrom.)

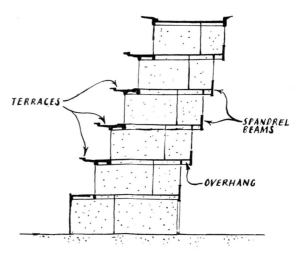

TERRACES

SPANDREL BEAMS

OVERHANG

CROSS - SECTION

Fig. 177, left and above, the Louis Pasteur Hospital at Colmar, France, where spandrel beams permit terracing at each floor level, resulting in a massing of articulated storeys. (Architect: William Vetter.)

*Fig. 178, above and right, house at Bear
Run, Pennsylvania, constructed of stone and
reinforced concrete, is a spacial composition which develops contemporary materials to the demands of a most unusual site.
(Architect: Frank Lloyd Wright.)*

mass relationship, the greatest scope seems to lie in the awakening of the plane of
enclosure itself. Thus we find the suspended restaurant in Stockholm (fig. 176),
enclosing a given volume in space and creating a new mass relationship between
itself and adjacent buildings. Reinforced concrete seems to be particularly suited
for this role due to its combined structural and space enclosing properties. A Hospital at Colmar, France (fig. 177), provides a good illustration of the contribution of
the reinforced concrete spandrel beam to the new aesthetic in massing. As shown in
the section, each successive storey is set back so as to create on the south side a
series of terraces in front of the wards. This produces a corresponding series of over-
hung storeys, made possible by the use of spandrel beams spanning thirty-five feet
between projecting buttress wings. This solution to the terrace problem might have
even greater possibilities in the design of multi-storey dwellings, producing a
massing relationship which involves complete articulation of each storey. A more
dramatic example is the well known house on a waterfall at Bear Run, Pennsylvania (fig. 178). Here, a complete spatial composition of inter-penetrating masses
and slabs develops contemporary materials to the demands of a most unusual site.
In one of his latest projects, Frank Lloyd Wright has made use of the efficiency of
circular monolithic forms. The design, which is for a Sports Club on top of a low
range of hills in Hollywood (fig. 179), incorporating three reinforced concrete
cantilevered bowls, containing swimming pool, lounge and restaurant, carried on a
central triangular stone trunk, produces a massing more reminiscent of a plant form
than anything we have ever seen in architecture.

Fig. 179, below, project for a sports club
in the hills of Hollywood uses stone and
reinforced concrete to produce a massing
closer to plant forms than anything previously seen in architecture. (Architect:
Frank Lloyd Wright.)

Contrasting approaches in massing

In the last two examples we see a massing firmly entrenched in the ground and growing out of it, but sprouting the branches of the new structure. The contrasting approach of another pioneer of contemporary architecture, Le Corbusier, is demonstrated in the Swiss hostel in Paris (fig. 180), where the roots, as it were, have emerged from the ground to support the building mass well clear of it. This is a literal interpretation of this structure, which has a raised platform of reinforced concrete to support the light steel frame of the building mass, displaying a deliberate attempt to dissociate the main body of the building from the ground, thus retaining a continuity of landscape and circulation. These two opposed interpretations of the freedom in massing produced by the new structural materials, have been described by Giedion as "the contemporary reflection of the difference between the Greek temple, sharply outlined against its background, and the mediaeval town attached like a plant to the site on which it stands."[24] It may be that one has its place in the urban scene in providing a light and unconfined background to the turbulence of city life, whilst the other might provide the best solution for the landscape setting, where the building must grow out of its surroundings in order to become a part of them. This means a reversal of historic associations; of the town attached to its site and the isolated temple standing out against nature. Social change might thus be reflected through the medium of structural development.

The skeleton frame, by producing the skyscraper slab as a successor to the solid tower or pyramid of non-tensile materials, has created a vertical emphasis of entirely new proportions. The modifying influence of vertical circulation is seen in the R.C.A. building (fig. 149) where the principle of providing a maximum depth of 27 ft. from the building core to the external walls, in order to give adequate light to the working area, has been carried to its logical conclusion by cutting back the building as each bank of elevators comes to an end.

[24] See "Space, Time and Architecture" page 413.

Fig. 180, above, the Swiss hostel in the University City, Paris, is constructed of a light steel frame supported on a raised platform of reinforced concrete, displaying a deliberate attempt to lift the building mass well clear of the ground. (Architects: Le Corbusier and P. Jeanneret.)

The development of the structural slab has produced monolithic forms, which, when combined with the point supports of the skeleton frame, provide greater flexibility in massing and structural composition. The stressed skin provides units of massing complete in themselves and offering the opportunity of combining curved shapes with rectilinear forms, a field which has been little exploited since the domes of the Renaissance. Monolithic construction restores attention to what have been called the great primary forms of architectural massing—cubes, cones, spheres, cylinders, pyramids and their variants—which may spring to life as distinct and independent units, related to each other and to the earth's surface as solidly or as lightly as the situation demands.

New flexibility in massing

Fig. 181, above, glass enclosure produces a massing of a fluctuating and ephemeral nature as seen in the Open-Air School at Clio Street, Amsterdam, Holland. (Architect: P. Bijvoet and J. Duiker.)

Variable massing of glass enclosures

A further aspect arises out of the use of glass for the enclosing skin, since the transparency of the material provides a variable effect in the nature of the massing. The actual glazing divisions obviously become of great importance, since in certain lights they may provide the only material effect of enclosure. In an open-air school at Amsterdam, (fig. 181), part of the reinforced concrete skeleton is enclosed and part is left open to form open-air terraces; the fluctuating and ephemeral nature of the glazing at different floors is clearly seen, and whilst it is sufficient to define the mass of that part which it encloses, there is enough continuity in the structure to bind the whole into one unit. The form of the exposed structure clearly plays an important part in massing of this kind and an outstanding example is the circular stair tower at the Trades School, Stockholm (fig. 182). The variability of massing value is well illustrated in the two photographs, the one close up where the form of the enclosure is fairly well defined, and the other in which the form of the spiral stair is the dominant factor with the massing merely suggestive in character. Light and shade which reveal the relationship between solid masses normally seen side by side, provide here a new relationship of one form placed within another, creating a further new factor in the aesthetics of massing, arising out of contemporary structural development.

Fig. 182, above and right, the glazed stair-case tower of the Trades School in Stock-holm, Sweden, demonstrates a further new factor in the aesthetics of massing, created by the relationship of one form placed within another. (Architect: P. Hedqvist.)

Structural Form

The structural shell provides an efficient use of material, since the stresses in it are due mainly to direct forces occurring in the surface of the shell and the disposition of material can therefore bear a close relationship to stress distribution, with little variation in the shell thickness. The replacement of a shell by a series of planes not only introduces bending moments but also greater stress variation due to the concentration of forces produced by the moments at the folds. Further breaking down of the structure into a skeleton frame clearly involves greater stress concentration accompanied by more uneven stress distribution within each member. Disposition of material according to the stresses involved might, therefore, be expected to produce a corresponding variation in the cross-section of the framing member, but other considerations normally require a compromise between the ideal and the practical.

Form and stress distribution

By means of an infinite control over matter, nature has created an aesthetic relationship between form and structural function. The forms of nature, which in the past provided a source of inspiration in painting and sculpture, could not be followed in the design of the architectural fabric until appropriate materials became available, and then only within the limited control possessed by man over materials. They were thus incorporated into architecture as applied decoration, providing an aesthetic contrast to the solid structural fabric whose form arose out of the stability of the non-tensile units, rather than the strength of the material. Giedion has pointed out how the static feelings associated with the architecture of self-evident stability were completely disrupted by the three-hinged steel arches of the Galerie des Machines at the 1889 Exhibition (fig. 183),[25] which seem to have heralded the move towards an aesthetic appropriate to the new materials. Steel as a material, however, did not at first lend itself to the refinement of structure characteristic of natural forms, and it was only with the full development of reinforced concrete, accompanied by increased knowledge of stress distribution, that greater attention was devoted to the aesthetics of contemporary structure. Although structural refinement is now possible with welded steel and laminated timber which can be molded to shape without involving the costs of complicated form-work, reinforced concrete seems to provide through its plastic nature, the widest opportunity for full development of structural form.

The aesthetic of natural forms

[25]See "Space, Time and Architecture," page 205.

Articulation of the hinged-joint

The hinged joint probably provides the strongest case for articulation, since it transmits force but not bending moment and a pin-jointed member therefore has no moments to resist at the hinges. Fig. 184 illustrates a showroom in Paris where the whole of the front is kept free of supports by the use of overhead trusses, and the vertical steel stiffeners of the immense glazed panel take their form from the stress distribution due to lateral forces. This form is equally applicable to compression members under similar conditions and has been used for circular columns in timber. A circular member of this form would probably be the most efficient as a strut and perhaps have the greatest aesthetic value, but a cruciform type would be a good compromise giving the benefit of the stress-conscious shape along two principal axes. In the case of beams, resistance to shear becomes an important factor and therefore tends to limit the refinement of form arising out of moment variation. Thus with heavy loads and short spans, there will probably be little scope in depth variation, although there is still opportunity for graduation in width. Various forms can be arrived at according to the material being used and depending on whether

164

Fig. 185, above, trussed beams of laminated timber spanning 90 ft. across the Recreation Building at the U. S. Naval Training Station, Great Lakes, Illinois, show a natural combination of refined form and economy in providing a graduated resistance moment. (Architects: Skidmore, Owings and Merrill. Engineers: Unit Structures, Inc.)

the beam is freely supported or continuous, but costs of fabrication would normally outweigh any advantage to be gained from the refinement of material. An interesting compromise is seen in the beams supporting the gallery of the Exhibition Hall at Turin (fig. 164), where variation in width below the compression flange produces a beam which is remarkably slender in the centre, with thickened roots at the supports to cope with the maximum shear forces and compression due to negative bending. For light loading, however, on freely supported members, the form can be more easily refined to provide a graduated resistance moment, as seen in the 90 ft. span laminated timber beams used at the Great Lakes Naval Training Station (fig. 185). These beams are supported on steel tubular columns, so that the vertical glazing divisions, which take no load, are of the same form employed in the Paris Showroom (fig. 184). The form of the reinforced concrete beams referred to in the previous chapter (fig. 27) was of the same kind, and steel has been used in a similar way.

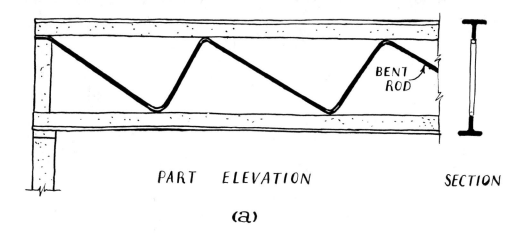

PART ELEVATION   SECTION

(a)

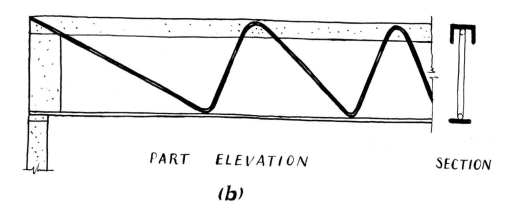

PART ELEVATION   SECTION

(b)

Fig. 186, left, built-up lattice girders in welded steel lend themselves to a frank expression of the forces at work, by means of careful economy in the design of the members. (Engineers: Messrs. Helsby, Hamann, and Samuely.)

Structural expression in composite members

Built-up members in welded steel seem to lend themselves to another form of expression which may be of value where they are to be exposed. Fig. 186a shows one example, built-up of tees as flanges and bent rod as the connecting web, where the form of the rod is governed by diagonal shear, providing a shorter length for compression in order to develop the same stress as in tension. A further development is shown in fig. 186b; here the slope of the rod is steeper towards the centre of the beam where shear diminishes, in order to provide more frequent support for the top flange as the compression stress due to bending, increases. The form of the bent rod, symbolising the simple harmonic motion of a pendulum, conveys the feeling of a change in the nature of the forces taking place along the length of the beam. This treatment of built-up members provides an aesthetic response akin to the variation in proportion of solid members, and is not normally present in the mechanical form of a conventional lattice girder. It is perhaps this uniformity in a conventional triangulated truss, which has prompted the suggestion that the pulling and pushing of adjacent members induces a sense of restlessness and lack of harmony, since there is little indication of stress variation to attract the attention and the eye is drawn only to the regular triangulation. It also seems probable that restlessness, to the unpractised eye, is caused by an inability to distinguish between members in tension and members in compression in a normal steel truss. This confusion is removed in the concrete truss shown earlier in fig. 26 by the clear distinction of tension members from those in compression, thereby introducing an aesthetic arising out of the combination of tension and compression in structure.

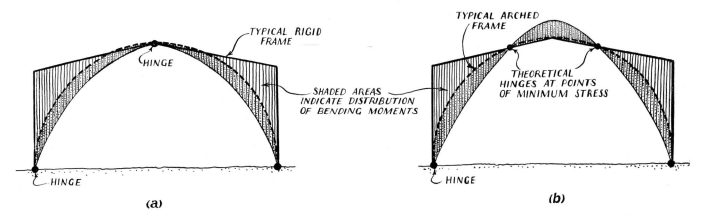

Fig. 187 A, above, the bending moment set up at any point in a three-hinged arch is governed by the extent to which the arch deviates from the parabola passing through the three hinges.

Fig. 187 B, above, the bending moment set up at any point in a two-hinged arch is governed by the extent to which the arch deviates from the parabola passing through the two base hinges and the two imaginary hinges at the points of minimum stress.

The importance of tension in the new aesthetic

The acceptance of the new aesthetic has probably been made more difficult by the fact that the tensile material has been introduced into structure without sufficient evidence of the part which it plays in combining with the long accepted forces of compression to create the new forms. It seems, therefore, that a clear distinction wherever possible between tension and compression members, might assist the human eye to grasp the meaning of the existence of both kinds of forces in contemporary architecture and thus appreciate the spirit of the new aesthetic. Such a distinction is particularly well expressed in the Swedish bridges illustrated earlier in fig. 57 which contrast the concrete compression arch with the slender steel suspension members supporting the platform; or again in the Airship Hangars at Orly (fig. 135) where steel tension rods are threaded through the corrugations of the compressive concrete arch to maintain the required shape.

Fig. 188, above, left and right, the road bridge over the river Thur near Felsegg, Switzerland, typifies the work of its designer in the structural refinement of its three-hinged box type arches of 236 ft. span which are merged into the roadway slab. (Engineer: Robert Maillart.)

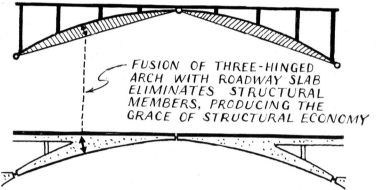

FUSION OF THREE-HINGED ARCH WITH ROADWAY SLAB ELIMINATES STRUCTURAL MEMBERS, PRODUCING THE GRACE OF STRUCTURAL ECONOMY

Refinement of arches and rigid frames

The use of arched forms provides greater scope in the field of structural refinement than beam and column construction. Firstly in the shaping of the arch as a whole, according to the conditions of loading, so as to produce the minimum of bending stresses, and secondly in the refinement of the arch limbs according to stress distribution, particularly where overall shape is governed by considerations other than structural ones, resulting in the setting up of bending moments. The ideal arch shapes for given conditions of loading are identical with those taken up by a freely suspended cable in pure tension for the same loading, since the cable is not capable of sustaining any bending stresses. It is found that whereas a circular form, so much used in the past, will result from a loading which is heavier towards the supports than at the centre, the type of distributed load normally encountered, will form the cable into a parabola. The latter is therefore the shape in which the arch conforms most closely to a state of pure compression under normal conditions of loading, and in the case of a rigid frame, bending moments are set up according to the deviation of the frame from the ideal arch shape. Thus, in a three-hinged arch or rigid frame, the extent to which the shape of the arch diverges at any given point from the parabola passing through the three hinges, will govern the bending moment set up, as illustrated in fig. 187a. The resulting forms are perhaps the most common examples of structural refinement, which can be seen in the illustrations of three-hinge arches in the previous chapter and also in the three-hinged box type arches (fig. 188) used in so many of Maillart's structurally refined bridges. The two-hinged arch or rigid frame, on the other hand, gives a more even distribution of moment as in a monolithic frame (fig. 187b), and as in the case of the latter, structural refinement is more difficult to achieve and is therefore less pronounced

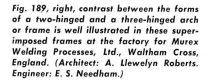

Fig. 189, right, contrast between the forms of a two-hinged and a three-hinged arch or frame is well illustrated in these superimposed frames at the factory for Murex Welding Processes, Ltd., Waltham Cross, England. (Architect: A. Llewelyn Roberts. Engineer: E. S. Needham.)

than in the case of the three-hinged frame. Reference to the examples in the previous chapter, however, indicates quite a varying degree of forms, in spite of these limitations. The contrast between the typical forms of two and three-hinged frames is well illustrated in the superimposed frames shown in fig. 189. The refined three-hinged frame expresses the distinction between the rigidity at the knee and the freedom at the hinges, the cantilevered form of the upper part displaying delicate refinement, since shear force and bending moment rise and fall together. The refined form of the cantilever has become such a common-place as to need no further comment and is seen very clearly in the open-air school at Amsterdam (fig. 181).

Fig. 190, right, cross-head cantilevers form the junction between cruciform columns and floor slabs at Peckham Health Centre, London. (Architect and Engineer: Sir E. Owen Williams.)

The form of slab on point supports

Since stress distribution in a monolithic skeleton frame is more even than in a nominally pin-jointed frame, less opportunity occurs for refinement, but with reinforced concrete, the use of the floor slab as a compression flange may require the introduction of haunches to resist the negative moments at supports; alternatively large shear forces may make this necessary. Thus the development of the floor slab into something more than mere infilling may affect the form of the remainder of the structure, if full economy is to be maintained, and the extreme case is the slab diaphragm supported only on columns. The enlargement of the column head, required to prevent a column from punching through a superimposed slab and to resist the high bending moment occurring over the column, has been solved in a variety of ways since the first example in Zurich (fig. 94). The hyperbolic profile of the column heads in the latter case, was the result of an attempt to provide a uniform shear stress in this region, and in later examples, as in fig. 193, the shape of the heads was designed to follow the variation in bending moments. At the Peckham Health Centre (fig. 190) the derivative form of cross-head cantilevers is used, in logical conjunction with cruciform columns. Between this and the circular column with circular mushroom head (fig. 95), there is obviously great scope for variation in shape. Great pyramidal heads (fig. 191) were employed in a factory at Beeston, England, whilst two octagonal forms, one used in France and the other in Switzerland, are shown in figs. 192 and 193. The two latter show a distinct aesthetic difference, the one self-contained, a hand as it were supporting a tray, and the other providing a continuous flow of form from column into slab in accordance with Maillart's strict analysis, portraying the monolithic nature of the whole and completely departing from the classic conception of the relationship between a column head and its load. The feeling of continuity is a purer structural expression, since the mushroom head can more accurately be regarded as a swelling of the slab preparatory to meeting the column. The conception of the mushrooms used in the building at Racine (fig. 158) is totally different, since the mushroom columns are self-contained structural units, inverted plungers as they have been described, which are sufficiently large in themselves to receive the slab direct.

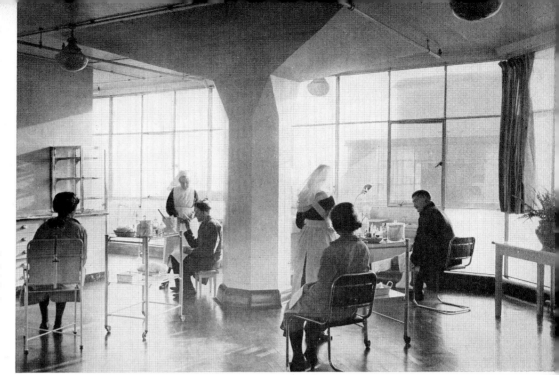

Fig. 191, right, the heavily loaded floor slabs of the factory for Messrs. Boots Pure Drug Co. at Beeston, England, are brought onto the supporting columns by means of large pyramidal heads. (Architect and Engineer: Sir E. Owen Williams.)

Fig. 192, left, octagonal shaped mushroom head in a building for Messrs. Hachette in France, expresses the action of a hand supporting a tray. (Architect: J. Demaret.)

Fig. 193, right, octagonal shaped mushroom head in the Federal Grain Store at Altdorf, Switzerland, is fused into the slab in a pure structural manner and expresses a swelling of the slab before it meets the column. (Engineer: Robert Maillart.)

Fig. 194, left and above, the stepped canopy in a house at Bear Run, Pennsylvania, which climbs with the slope of the steep hillside, is carried on point supports by using the vertical folds as cantilevers. (Architect: Frank Lloyd Wright.)

Structural shape and stress distribution

The stepped canopy in the house at Bear Run, Pennsylvania (fig. 194) consists of a slab in a continuous folded form, supported on columns under the vertical folds, which thereby become cantilevers, and the necessity for the kind of swelling between column and slab just described is eliminated. Direct stressing in the plane of the slab which produces a more even distribution of forces, introduces automatically an overall structural refinement resulting from an economical use of material. Compare for instance, the railway platform canopy constructed of beam, column and slab (fig. 195) with a similar canopy constructed of a shell between cantilever frames (fig. 196). The distribution of stress becomes apparent in the smoother flow of lines and reduction of material, carrying with it the aesthetic of primary forms. The frames required for maintaining the shapes of shell elements can obviously be refined in the same way as a normal skeleton frame but the shell itself is normally incapable of taking point loads, so that it is not likely to produce forms comparable to the swellings introduced in combining slab and column. A characteristic refinement, however, is the stiffening rib introduced to absorb increased local stresses as was shown in fig. 123. Where the supporting ribs are placed above the shell a completely smooth flow of lines and surfaces is obtained, creating a feeling of lightness which is especially valuable in the roofing of a large open area such as the Tennis Hall in Copenhagen (fig. 197). The flow of structural shape reaches its ultimate conclusion in the corrugated shell roof at Copenhagen Airport (fig. 198) which virtually floats on its supports.

Fig. 196, below, railway platform canopy of a shell between cantilever frames at Malden Manor Station, England. (Engineers: Messrs. Chisarc and Shell 'D'.)

Fig. 195, above, railway platform canopy of beam, column and slab at Stamford Brook Station, England.

Fig. 197, right, the shell concrete roof of the K. B. Tennis Hall in Copenhagen, Denmark, demonstrates the smooth flowing lines resulting from the more even stress distribution which accompanies an economical use of material. (Architects: Hans Hansen. Engineer: C. Ostenfeld.)

Fig. 198, above, the corrugated shell concrete roof over the departure hall at Copenhagen Airport, Denmark, carries the flow of structural shape to its ultimate conclusion, creating a covering which virtually floats on its supports. (Architect: Vilhelm Lauritzen. Engineer: Chr. Noekkentved.)

The actual distribution of stress clearly affects the relationship of framing members, so that even if we do not employ a stressed slab or skin, the use of the two-way span and mutually supporting members provides a levelling out of stress which approaches much more closely the aesthetic of primary forms. Continuous construction, such as the diagonal grid type, is the most suitable for providing this result. Fig. 199 shows a church at Manchester, England, where the structural members have all been carefully related to each other by this means, producing a form close to that of a flat slab on mushroom-headed columns. Even where the stresses cannot be so evenly distributed, a careful and harmonious relationship between structural members can, by providing a systematic arrangement, enable the pattern of structural forces to play its fundamental role in architectural design (see fig. 200).

Fig. 199, right, the ceiling of a church at Manchester, England, where a careful relationship of mutually supporting members approaches the aesthetic of the flat slab form. (Architect: N. F. Cachemaille-Day. Engineers: Diagrid Structures, Ltd.)

Fig. 200, left, ground floor construction of the Technical College at Berne, Switzerland shows a careful and harmonious relationship between beams and cantilevers on the one hand and between beams and columns on the other. (Architects: H. Brechbuhler; Dubach and Gloor.)

Integration of form and function

The degree to which function will influence the form of structure will depend upon the nature of the latter. The complete shell enclosure such as that shown in fig. 148, is obviously governed by functional considerations; the form of the stepped slab at Bear Run (fig. 194) results from the adaptation of a function to the requirements of a particular site; and the spiral slabs at the London Zoo (fig. 201) are born of the need for ramps with minimum supports. In skeleton framing, function has less influence on the form of the individual member, but as mentioned earlier in the chapter, there seem to be opportunities for making structural members perform additional duties. For instance, the beam and column may both perform the function of duct enclosures, the former being demonstrated in the spandrel beams at the Finsbury Health Centre, London (fig. 167). With the increasing tendency towards the use of large monolithic structural members, the conception of the staircase as a single structural unit designed for a particular function, has received greater attention; either as a central core with stair slab wound around it as seen in fig. 202, or developed into a complete spiral element (fig. 203) taking its place with the horizontal and vertical elements of the skeleton frame (fig. 204). The spiral is probably the most interesting form of staircase element, used often in the past as a straightforward solution to the problem presented and necessarily employing a central supporting core. The ability to eliminate this central support by means of contemporary structure is resulting in the appearance of forms of great sculptural value as is well illustrated in the staircase of the Air Terminal Building, at Rio de Janeiro (fig. 205). What is probably the longest self-supporting spiral stair, in this case in steel in a factory in S. Wales (fig. 206), was the result of a challenge which subsequently proved to have no basis since the stair which initiated the challenge was later discovered to have a central support. These staircase forms are significant beyond the interior by virtue of the glass enclosure.

Fig. 204, below, the entrance to the Instituto De Desseguros Do Brazil showing the curved concrete stairway taking its place as a structural element with the vertical and horizontal elements of the skeleton frame.

Fig. 203, above, steel staircase in the Holland Building, Rockefeller Centre, New York is a complete spiral element whose form is accentuated by the plate glass balustrade. (Architects: Reinhard and Hofmeister; Corbett, Harrison and MacMurray; Hood and Fouilhoux.)

Fig. 205, below, spiral staircase of reinforced concrete in the Air Terminal Building, Rio de Janeiro, Brazil, is developed into a form of great sculptural interest. (Architects: Marcelo, Milton and Mauricio Roberto. Engineer: Glebe Saharov.)

Fig. 206, above, steel spiral staircase in the factory for Enfield Cables, Ltd. at Brynmawr, Wales, is remarkable for the complete absence of any central support in so long a spiral. (Architects: Architects' Cooperative Partnership. Engineers: Ove Arup and Partners.)

Fig. 207, above, the Colosseum, Rome, displays the superimposing of the post and lintel form on arch construction, a development which helped to sow the seeds of facade architecture.

Expression

Divorce of expression from structural feeling

The development of the pilaster by the Romans would seem to have played a great part in the divorce of architectural expression from structural feeling; for even where it performed a structural function as a buttress, its duties bore no relationship to its form and associations. The patterning of surfaces by means of superimposing the post and lintel form on arch construction, (fig. 207), was a contradiction in terms and therefore a negation of structural aesthetic. It failed to hide the fact that the arch was the principal structural form, but helped to sow the seeds of facade architecture, which was to be so ruinous to the development of architectural expression when structure was released from the limitations of the load-bearing wall. The result is to be found in a public taste which has failed to appreciate the significance of contemporary structure or to cultivate the feelings which it engenders, and which, mostly, still prefers the massive forms natural to non-tensile materials to the free and dynamic elegance of the new structural materials.

Fig. 208, left, the Guildhall at Thaxted, Essex, typical of the timber frame as developed in England, is the outcome of a straight-forward combination of tensile and non-tensile materials.

Traditional idioms derived from the structure

Since architectural expression is the outcome of the many complex factors which govern the composition, it must logically be based upon structure, which alone makes building possible. This does not mean necessarily the exposure of structure; as Le Corbusier has said, "architecture has another meaning and other ends to pursue, than showing construction and responding to needs." It means, however, the recognition of structure as the life force, and an architectural expression true to the nature of its materials. The Gothic builders developed out of a non-tensile material the form of frame and infilling, which nevertheless retained the essential structural unity of a single material, thereby producing a universal idiom arising out of the nature of that material. The timber frame as used in England (fig. 208) introduced the tensile frame with non-tensile infilling, involving the exposure of the structural frame as the outcome of a straightforward combination of materials. On the other hand, American clap-board construction (fig. 209) is an equally logical result of combining a tensile cladding with a tensile frame, which acknowledges the structure without exposing it. These examples suggest that the freedom of architectural expression introduced by contemporary structure must retain its allegiance to the nature of materials, if structure is to maintain its traditional place in architectural evolution.

Fig. 210, above, Lower Manhattan, New York City. Romantic towers which on closer approach solidify into towering un-buttressed walls of brick or masonry quite unrelated to the nature of these materials and giving no indication of their passive structural role. (Photo by Ewing Galloway, N. Y.)

Human sensation and the nature of materials

Human sensation is closely bound up with experience. A structure clothed in glass is felt through the medium of the fragile glass, even if it is not evident by means of its transparency. On the other hand, a structure clothed in and supporting a stone or brick enclosure, may be denied by the way in which the materials are combined. The towers of Lower Manhattan stand out from across the water as romantic symbols of contemporary structural achievement (fig. 210) but as one approaches them, they solidify into towering unbuttressed walls of brick or masonry with regular piercings from top to bottom, which give no reassurance of their passive structural role and are therefore so unrelated to the nature of the materials as to be overwhelming to the unaccustomed eye. Although this phenomenon is less evident in buildings of average height normally encountered in the U.S.A. and other countries, it serves as a reminder that the contribution of the tensile structure and the non-tensile cladding must both be recognised in architectural expression, if the new structure is to form the basis of an architectural idiom characteristic of our time.

Fig. 211, above and right, a carefully proportioned relationship of welded steel frame with brick and glass infilling in a building of the Illinois Institute of Technology. (Architect: Ludwig Mies van der Rohe.)

What is perhaps the most direct approach is to be found in the new group of buildings for the Illinois Institute of Technology in Chicago, one of which is illustrated in fig. 211; this shows a clear and straightforward combination of materials based on a carefully proportioned relationship of welded steel frame with brick and glass infilling. Although exposure of the structure in this manner requires considerable refinement of detail, it seems to offer great scope with the development of welding and possible new protective materials. The aesthetic value to be obtained from a carefully proportioned relationship of materials in this manner, continues the tradition which was started with the brick-nogging of the timber frame. Its application to multi-storey buildings seems likely to be limited as far as steel is concerned, so long as standard rolled sections are in predominant use, since it is difficult to obtain vertical members having the constant width desirable both for appearance and economy, without being wasteful in material. It is an idiom, however, which has been developed in reinforced concrete in France, following the example of Auguste Perret as early as 1903 (fig. 212). By virtue of its flexibility, either in the

Fig. 212, left, No. 25 bis Rue Franklin, Paris, in which the reinforced concrete frame was used as an expressive architectural element as early as 1903. (Architect: Auguste Perret.) Above, a house at Garches, France, with reinforced concrete frame exposed and concrete slab infilling unbonded to express its passive role. (Architects: A. and G. Perret.)

the variation of quantity of reinforcement or in permitting columns to be poured to a constant width, reinforced concrete makes it easier to obtain a regular rhythm in the facade. This is seen on a small scale in the Technical College at Berne, Switzerland (fig. 213), which displays a sensitively proportioned structure and an architectural expression true to the nature of the materials. In this case the column size has been kept constant through four storeys, whereas reference to fig. 160 will show how a constant width of column was maintained through eleven storeys in the Plaslaan apartments in Rotterdam, Holland. The regular rhythm of the facade can be seen in fig. 214 and it constitutes not only a method of structural expression but also a true representation of the nature of the building—a series of superimposed dwellings.

Fig. 213, above and left, the Technical College at Berne, Switzerland, a multi-storey building in which the sensitively proportioned reinforced concrete structure provides the basis for an architectural expression true to the nature of the materials of which it is composed. (Architects: H. Brechbuhler; Dubach and Gloor.)

Fig. 214, below, the Plaslaan apartment building in Rotterdam, Holland, displays the regular rhythm resulting from its structure and expresses its nature as a series of superimposed dwellings. (Architects: W. van Tijen and H. A. Maaskant.)

Fig. 215, above, an apartment building in Copenhagen, Denmark, in which is expressed both the structural planes of its box-frame construction, and the cellular nature of the building. (Architect: Mogens Lassen. Engineer: Ernst Ishoy.)

Box-frame construction presents a much stronger case for this form of expression in certain instances, since it introduces the structural plane which provides a clear statement of subdivision. The frame seen on elevation has little or no depth, but the end of a structural plane can be difficult to deny, since it tells a double story of structure and the cellular nature of the building. An apartment building of box-frame construction in Copenhagen, shown in fig. 215, follows this complete expression, while fig. 216 illustrates a project for a hostel based on the same system of construction, in which the unit of purpose expressed through the structure is the individual rather than the dwelling. A modified form of this type of expression was used in a building of duplex apartments in London (fig. 217) where the box wall has only been exposed at alternate floors; nevertheless, the passive role of the brick infilling panels remains clearly apparent.

Fig. 216, above, project for a students' Hostel in London in which the unit of purpose expressed through the structure is the individual rather than the dwelling. (Architect: Leonard Michaels.)

Fig. 217, right, a duplex apartment building at Kenmure Road, London, expresses the passive role of the brick panel walls without complete exposure of its box-frame walls. (Architect: Edward D. Mills. Engineer: Ove Arup and Partners.)

Fig. 218, left, checkered reflection of the slender framework created by the large units of fenestration in the Carson, Pirie, Scott Department Store, Chicago, expresses the nature of the structure without actually exposing it. (Architect: Louis Sullivan.)

Fig. 219, right, the steel framework of the auditorium in the Entertainments Pavilion, Bexhill, England, is reflected in the cement rendered concrete walls by means of vertical expansion joints picked out in color. (Architects: Eric Mendelsohn and Serge Chermayeff. Engineers: Messrs. Helsby, Hamann and Samuely.)

The nature of the structure

Expression of the structure should display not only a true relationship of materials, but also the feeling of the nature of the frame itself, collecting and transferring its loads without emphasis on either the horizontal or the vertical. Louis Sullivan showed how this feeling could be expressed without resorting to the full exposure of the frame. Fig. 218 shows the department store in Chicago which he designed at the turn of the century, where the area of fenestration is such as to leave on the elevation only the checkered reflection of the slender framework behind. The regular rhythm of fenestration is made to express the structure and the non-tensile facing material becomes apparent for what it is.

Fig. 220, above, theatre at Utrecht, Holland, showing the steel columns of the stage tower expressed by means of rainwater pipes placed where the columns occur and picked out in color. (Architect: W. M. Dudok.)

Where the structure is not fully exposed, treatment of the cladding may provide the key to structural expression. Thus the elimination of bond from stone or brick facing, as seen in fig. 213, can reveal its true nature, at any rate from close quarters, and accentuation of the fact should assist in making it apparent even at a distance. The strength required in a brick panel wall is in the transverse direction to resist wind pressure or other lateral forces. In this respect bond is unlikely to be of much importance, but if it is retained, the true expression would seem to consist of the breaking of bond between panels or the articulation of the support obtained at each floor. Such methods of reflecting the structure in the panel wall show how a subtle use of materials can contribute towards structural expression. At Bexhill Pavilion, in England (fig. 219) vertical expansion joints in the cement rendering are picked out in colour and reflect the steel framework behind. The same effect was produced in a theatre at Utrecht, Holland (fig. 220) by means of rainwater downpipes which are brought boldly down the face of the stage tower where the steel columns occur, and are picked out against the facing tiles of the external wall.

Reflection of structure in the external veneer

Fig. 221, left, the Van Nelle Factory, Rotterdam, Holland, the first building in which mushroom construction was used as a means of architectural expression, to create a new kind of horizontality arising out of the structure. (Architect: J. A. Brinkman and L. C. van der Vlugt.)

Structurally free exteriors create a new expression

In contrast to the cage frame of one-dimensional members, the combination of horizontal slab with vertical framing members introduces a new and indisputable element into architectural expression. Although mushroom construction had been used as early as 1910, its architectural potentialities seem to have been ignored for nearly twenty years and it was probably not until 1927, in the Van Nelle factory at Rotterdam, Holland (fig. 221), that the first significant architectural development was born of this construction. The continuous glass screen, made possible by the elimination of columns from the external wall, may be either a complete unpunctuated enclosure as in the Bauhaus at Dessau, Germany (fig. 222), or continuous between floors as in the factory at Beeston, England (fig. 223), where the exposed floor slabs take on the form of string courses to the glass facade, with the structural columns providing a soft accompaniment in the background. Alternatively, the use of solid spandrels, as in the Van Nelle factory, creates a horizontality arising out of the structure and quite unrelated to former uses of non-tensile materials. The

Fig. 222, above, the Bauhaus at Dessau, Germany shows the glass screen as a complete unpunctuated enclosing element. (Architect: Walter Gropius.)

Fig. 223, below, the factory for Messrs. Boots Pure Drug Co. at Beeston, England, shows how the exposed floor slabs take on the form of string courses to the glass facade. (Architect and Engineer: Sir E. Owen Williams.)

Fig. 224, above and left, in the Schocken Store at Chemnitz, Germany, cantilevered external bays result in spandrel girders alternated with continuous bands of glazing, through which the cantilevers tell their story. (Architect: Eric Mendelsohn.)

Fig. 225, right, the structural pattern of the Longfellow Building in Washington, D.C. is clarified by the combination of cantilevered floor slabs on one elevation with horizontal bands and occasionally visible columns on the other. (Architect: William Lescaze.)

external wall will automatically be made as light as possible, since it has only a slab to support it. The cantilevered end bay, which is the natural form of continuous construction, invokes a similar form of expression to the flat slab, and the horizontality of the solid spandrel alternated with continuous glazing is, therefore, an equally logical outcome of monolithic construction. This is well illustrated in the department store at Chemnitz, Germany (fig. 224) where the 15 feet cantilevers of the end bays tell their structural story, with particular emphasis at night, through the horizontal bands of glazing; and the solid spandrels appear for what they are, as light girdles supported on the cantilevered beams. With the use of the solid spandrel, however, the horizontal slab becomes subdued by the bold lines of the enclosing wall surface, and fails to register in the overall composition. In the Longfellow Building at Washington, D. C. (fig. 225), advantage has been taken of a corner site to cantilever the floor slabs into balconies on one elevation, and these combine with the horizontal bands and occasionally visible columns on the other, to give a clear picture of the structural pattern.

Fig. 226, left, the Parklaan apartment building in Rotterdam, Holland, is faced with sheet material whose framed enclosures demonstrate their passive role. (Architect: W. van Tijen.)

Fig. 227, right, Highpoint 1 apartments at Highgate, London, show the greater freedom in fenestration made possible by the structural external wall slab. (Architects: Tecton. Engineers: J. L. Kier and Co., Ltd.)

Expression of tensile materials

The use of tensile materials for the external skin presents a different problem. Sheet materials will normally be supported in frames as seen in an apartment building in Rotterdam, Holland (fig. 226), or will otherwise indicate their nature. Reinforced concrete introduces into the expression of the external wall a monolithic material, providing structural support to a multi-storey building in contrast to the brick or stone panel wall, which exists only by reason of the hidden supporting frame. An apartment block at Highgate, London (fig. 227) shows how this use of reinforced concrete permits a greater freedom in fenestration, which is no longer governed by the structural grid. It becomes all the more important that any facing material employed should be applied in such a manner as to make its passive role self-evident, so that the monolithic nature of the structural wall is not lost.

Fig. 228, the Saurer office building at Arbon, Switzerland, expresses the nature of the materials employed by means of something more than pure exposure of the structure. (Architects: G. P. Dubois and J. Eschenmoser.)

Structure as a base pattern

The string course of the load bearing wall often constituted an expression of the structure behind, and the punctuation of a brick panel wall to express its true character might be regarded as its equivalent. It also contributed, however, to the architectural patterning of the wall surface which was therefore related to a certain extent to the internal structure. Contemporary materials provide a much greater incentive for the use of the structure as a base pattern in view of its repetitive character. Fig. 228 shows a block of offices at Arbon, Switzerland, where each floor is fully articulated and the rhythm of the pattern is provided by the column spacing. It demonstrates an expression true to the materials employed, which relies on something more than the showing of structure. The horizontality, which in this instance accentuates the support given to the brick infilling panels, is relieved by a gentle vertical emphasis, resulting in a pattern which expresses the strictly impartial nature of the structural frame. A pattern based on the column grid is simplest to obtain when the columns themselves are placed sufficiently close to become light

Fig. 229, above and right, the Columbus House, Berlin, in which the distinct vertical emphasis of the closely spaced columns is restored to its true importance by the horizontality of the self-evident spandrel facing panels applied in accordance with the structural pattern. (Architect: Eric Mendelsohn.)

mullions, between which standard windows and spandrel panels can be placed. If at the same time the loads are collected on cross beams, so that the horizontal members are only light ties as seen in the Columbus House, Berlin (fig. 229), a very distinct vertical emphasis is produced on the elevation. This, however, is no more representative of the structure as a whole, than an unrelieved horizontal emphasis would have been in the case of the building at Arbon. In this case, therefore, we find relief introduced in the horizontal direction. This can already be seen in the unfinished parts, where the columns remain visible between the solid spandrels supported on the ties, and by means of repetition the latter create a horizontal balance, producing a result similar to that in the Arbon building but arrived at in a different way. The horizontal support, however, which expresses the true nature of an exposed masonry infilling, is finally obscured in the case of the Columbus House, by the large facing panels applied in such a way as to be self-evident in character and retaining the continuity of the vertical supports through the joints between them.

Fig. 230, above, Peter Jones Store, London. Restrained vertical emphasis of what is clearly a screen wall seems to express the way in which loads are collected and transferred. (Architects: William Crabtree associated with Slater and Moberly and Prof. C. H. Reilly.)

It is clear that vertical and horizontal emphasis require very careful consideration in relation to the structure as a whole, if they are not to lead to excesses which are completely alien to the architectural expression of contemporary structure, and which merely exploit the freedom which it provides. Nevertheless, there remains a wide field for the creative artist to explore, with structural feeling as the motive power of his efforts, and a frank admission of the nature of materials as his guiding philosophy. For instance, although we have seen that free external walls have introduced an extreme horizontality, with the vertical elements of structure trickling out only through the filter of the glass enclosure, the London department store shown in fig. 230, which has all outside columns set well back from the external wall, displays a restrained vertical emphasis which brings the expression of load transfer into the plane of enclosure of the building. Although similar as a whole, to the treatment of the Columbus building in Berlin, the vertical emphasis in this instance bears no actual relationship to the irregularly placed internal columns and therefore

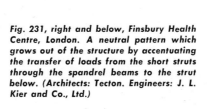

Fig. 231, right and below, Finsbury Health Centre, London. A neutral pattern which grows out of the structure by accentuating the transfer of loads from the short struts through the spandrel beams to the strut below. (Architects: Tecton. Engineers: J. L. Kier and Co., Ltd.)

expresses the structure in a less direct manner. It relies on the lightness of slender vertical mullions interwoven with the glass-faced spandrel beams suggestive of tensile materials, to portray its function as a screen and yet reflect the way in which loads are collected and transferred to the ground. Although there is a close relationship between the treatments of restrained and qualified emphasis employed in the last three examples, it is interesting to see how the brick panel finds its place in the building at Arbon but is alien to the aesthetic of the other two. An unusual problem was that presented in the case of the Health Centre in London previously illustrated (fig. 167), where the structure consists of short closely spaced struts and channel shaped spandrel beams, all in the external wall. The bare structure would have provided a conflict of alternating vertical and horizontal emphasis, but as seen in fig. 231 it has been used in a more subtle manner as the basis for a pattern which provides no emphasis in either direction, but yet expresses the structure by accentuating the transfer of load through the spandrel beam from each strut to the one below.

Fig. 232, Paimio Sanatorium, Finland. The motion of mechanical circulation, itself a by-product of contemporary structural development, is introduced into architectural composition. (Architect: Alvar Aalto.)

Vertical circulation

The influence which structure was shown to have had on 'plan', by reason of the increased importance of circulation, has obviously resulted in comparable repercussions in the field of architectural expression. Skyscrapers, where mechanical transport is the principal means of circulation, do not require such great attention to staircases which are, therefore, often without natural light. However, lighting of staircases in lower buildings, where they are important elements of circulation, introduces an essentially vertical element into elevational expression in contrast to the rest of the structure. Whilst this has been handled in many ways, from the complete glass panel to the piercing of small holes, the expression of mechanical circulation is not so familiar. It appears, however, in a Sanatorium in Finland (fig. 232), where the lift shaft is completely glazed, so that the mechanical movement of circulation is introduced into the composition, expressing the results of structural development.

Self-expression of the stressed skin

Compared with the skeleton frame, the stressed skin introduces restrictions on expression just as in other aspects of architectural design, but at the same time it provides less opportunity for denial of the structure. Moreover, its emphasis on form is likely to overshadow the importance of more detailed expression. It contributes towards the use of larger plane surfaces in the same way as the structural slab, relying on texture, fenestration and the effects of light and shade to produce an architectural expression true to the nature of the material.

Appendix

Contemporary Structural Materials

The architect today is remote from the materials of which his buildings are made; he relies on specialists to convey to him the dry bones of technical information which he is often incapable of assimilating and which fails to give him that feeling of a material which accompanies the close association of a craftsman. The architect must come to terms with this situation if he is to keep his creative art abreast of technical progress. He can only do this through a close understanding of that factor which governs the realisation of structural creation — the nature of available materials.

MATERIALS

Structural development is dependent upon improvements in the properties of materials and advances in the technique of their application. In order to appreciate present development and future possibilities, we must therefore examine the significant factors influencing the use of potential as well as established structural materials. For this purpose the following materials can be considered:—

a) Steel.

b) Reinforced concrete.

c) Timber.

d) Aluminium alloys.

The brief surveys which follow are not intended in any way to be comprehensive but rather aim at analysing the principal current developments in contemporary structural materials on the assumption that the reader is familiar with their earlier forms and applications.

STEEL

The introduction of iron into building construction about a century and a half ago began the new era in structure. In its early form—as cast iron—it was comparatively weak in tension; as wrought iron it could be used in conjunction with cast iron to compensate for this defect but it displayed a lack of uniformity in the material. It was only with its conversion into what we call mild steel, about a century ago, that iron was made available as a material having a uniform quality suitable for the application of mechanical science. Today it is a strictly controlled material, possessing known characteristics, and having a constant and uniform elasticity. In addition, it is available in varying grades up to a strength of 5 or 6 times that of mild steel.

One of the advantages of steel is that it is a very dense material and hence is capable of sustaining considerable stresses per unit area, which is of such value in multi-storey construction with its concentrated loading. At the same time this very fact means that it is poor in terms of flexural rigidity, making it liable to buckling when under compression. This means either that it must be shaped in such a way as to increase flexural rigidity, as for instance in bending a steel sheet into corrugated or other similar form, or alternatively the working stress must be reduced according to the buckling tendency, in which case the full strength of the material cannot be developed. The I-beam was produced as the solution to the resistance of bending stresses requiring widely separated areas, and its early use was in conjunction with circular cast-iron columns. This was an efficient combination since a circular section can provide a uniform and high flexural rigidity, and, in fact, a hollow tube is the most efficient structural shape for a member in compression. The use of the hollow tube, however, has been limited owing to difficulties of connection, except in very large scale work such as the Forth Bridge in Scotland, but the development of welding promises to overcome this difficulty, as shown in Chapter I. Its main use so far seems to have been in built-up members such as roof trusses and bridge girders (see fig. A.1.), but it obviously has wider applications in welded structures. Wide-flange shapes provide a more uniform flexural rigidity than standard rolled sections but there is still a loss of strength involved when they are used in compression, which may be quite considerable. This same lack of flexural rigidity may make itself felt even in the compression flanges of I-shapes used in bending, where there is insufficient lateral support to the beam. In fact, the disposition of material in rolled structural shapes is not the most efficient for some of the applications to which they must be put, and this is not easily remedied since the rolling process itself imposes limitations in the design of the sections. The alternative method of obtaining a more efficient structural section is, of course, to build it up out of smaller units, but the cost of fabrication must be set against the possible saving in material, and it is here that economy is likely to vary from one country to another or even from place to place, depending on the cost ratio between labour and material.

Fig. A 1, tubular steel footbridge over the River Alport, England.

Structural Members

So long as riveting or bolting were the sole means of joining one piece of steel to another, the use of built-up sections was mainly confined to larger structural members, but with the introduction of welding and the greater use of steel for smaller types of structure, there has been a tendency towards the development of lighter built-up members, disposing the material so as to resist the forces involved in a more efficient manner. The built-up member shown in Chapter II for instance (see fig. 186b) has a compression chord of different section from the tension chord and designed to resist the buckling tendency referred to above. Light open-web joists have been developed not only from the welding of small sections in this way, but also by the expanding of rolled shapes either by slitting on the principle of metal lath, or by cutting and re-welding so that the flanges are further apart. These members have a higher ratio of depth to weight than standard rolled shapes and are therefore very suitable for the attainment of long spans in lightly-loaded structures. Similarly welding simplifies the fabrication of hollow compression members from rolled shapes such as channels or angles, and these may be of lattice form similar to the open web joists. In all these built-up members, however, the cost of fabrication is an important factor and at the same time the weight of the members is governed by the thickness of metal in the rolled sections from which they are mostly built.

The idea of forming the structural shapes out of thin steel sheets was developed when the use of iron for building was still in its infancy, and thin iron sheets, cold-formed and riveted into I-beams, were used as long ago as 1855 in the U.S.A. in a building which lasted nearly 50 years.[26] Welding has had a considerable influence on the development of cold-formed sections of thin sheet steel for smaller types of structure, and from about 1930 onwards light gauge steel seems to have been introduced fairly generally as an economical alternative to timber for moderate loads and spans, mainly in house construction. Fig. A.2. shows a factory in England constructed entirely of pressed steel members, and light gauge steel structures seem to have been used on a considerable scale in the U.S.A. during World War II. In fact research has apparently been under way since before the war to develop the design of structural members formed of sheet steel, especially in relation to problems of local instability which arise in the case of thin unstiffened material. Amongst other things, attention has been given to the design of thin-walled columns which might be very efficient compression members if local instability could be overcome by distributing more evenly the tendency of the thin material to fail by buckling.

Jointing and Assembly

When steel was first used for building, the members were too large to be heated in the fire for forge-welding,[27] hence riveting or bolting came into use, introducing serious restrictions and disadvantages, such as unsightly connections, limitations of structural shapes, waste of material and the difficulty of obtaining rigid joints. Although considerable progress in welding had already been made in the U. S. A. and on the Continent of Europe before World War II, welding was developed greatly

[26]See Milton Male "Light Gauge Steel for Peacetime Building" in Engineering News-Record, Oct. 18th, 1945.

[27]See A. Ramsey Moon "Recent Experience in the Design of Welded Frames" in Journal of the Royal Institute of British Architects, May, 1944.

during the war years particularly through shipbuilding, with improvement in design and standardisation of details.[28] It enables rigid joints to be made which have the full strength of the pieces joined, without any appreciable increase of thickness or

Fig. A 2, left and below, framework of a plant at Hayes, England, constructed entirely of thin sheet steel. The tied arches have a span of 60 ft. and columns are hollow boxes filled with vibrated concrete. (Architect: H. V. Milnes Emerson. Engineers: Messrs. Helsby, Hamann and Samuely.)

weakening of the section such as occurs in riveting. By means of welding, steel becomes a more easily moulded material and members can be shaped more readily to conform with stress distribution. Light lattice members, rigid frames and the use of light-gauge steel are all facilitated, making steel more adaptable to architectural requirements. At the same time, the standard rolled sections which were designed for bolting or riveting are in many instances not very suitable for welding and developments seem to be taking place in the production of modified sections more suitable for the purpose. Although saving in the weight of material may be quite considerable, especially in the case of completely rigid frames, the overall cost, as mentioned in Chapter I, is at present not reduced by any means in an equal ratio. Overall economy seems to be most noticeable in heavy construction, but cost depends very much on the availability of welding operators and equipment, so that the full economy of welding may not show until it is used to a much greater extent. Bolted or riveted field connections permit welding to be confined to the shop, and may be the most economical method at present, except in the case of large structures or important rigid connections,[29] but joints have to be carefully located in order to retain the advantages of continuity (see fig. 10).

[28]See La Motte Grover "Development in Welded Steel Construction" in Engineering News-Record, October 18th, 1945.

[29]See F. J. Samuely "Welding" in The Architect and Building News, July 3rd, 1942.

Durability

The necessity to protect steel against atmospheric corrosion is a serious disadvantage and a particularly important factor to be considered in the use of thin sheet steel as a structural material. Although stainless steel requires no protection due to the formation of a self-healing film and even the resistance of ordinary steel in a normal atmosphere can be increased by the presence of a small copper content, the type of steel used in most cases, requires the protection of paint when left exposed. The cleaner lines of a welded structure provide less opportunity for hidden corrosion to occur and at the same time facilitate the periodical painting required for this protection. More usually, prevention of corrosion is combined with protection against fire, until now in the form of the concrete casing. The development of sprayed asbestos and experiments made with vermiculite promise to provide a much lighter form of protection, since the required thickness of the material for normal standards of protection would appear to be comparatively small. In conventional steel framed multi-storey structures, however, protection is provided by a great weight of solid concrete, which until recently was not allowed for as performing any structural role, and this has been a source of much controversy. It is claimed, firstly, that the concrete casing imparts considerable rigidity to a steel framed structure and secondly, that the concrete assists in resisting the loads. Even though the Codes both in England and in the U. S. A. now permit a small increase of stress for encased members, the weight of material seems to be out of all proportion to its structural value, so that development on the lines mentioned above might well contribute to a greatly increased efficiency of the multi-storey steel frame.

Developments in Application

The application of steel for structural purposes has developed well beyond its early use in the essentially one-dimensional form which had been established by the natural state of previously known structural materials. The use of sheet steel shows a new approach in applying the material, since it can either be formed into individual skeleton framing members, or, by suitable folding or corrugation, into structural panels or slabs. It can also be used in spherical or cylindrical form as a complete shell, as shown in Chapter I, so that it can now be applied to the complete structural range, from the concentration of loads in relatively few framing members to the dispersion of loads through the medium of a stressed enclosing skin.

At the same time there seems so far to have been a rather complete division between structures built entirely of rolled steel shapes even when used in conjunction with concrete, and those using steel bars or rods to co-operate with concrete in forming reinforced concrete structures. Here again developments can be seen, however. The U. S. Code now provides not only for an increased stress allowance for suitably encased columns, but also for the use of composite columns, consisting of a structural steel or cast-iron core encased in concrete, with the addition of both longitudinal and transverse reinforcement. Recommendations for the use of composite construction were made in England, on the grounds that in many instances an economical and rapid form of construction might consist of a light steel frame designed to carry temporary loads and subsequently encased with additionally reinforced concrete to assist in carrying the permanent loads. This method was used in the two apartment blocks referred to in Chapter I (see page 9). In the case of the eight-storey block at Leeds (fig. 5), where the welded frames were erected as complete units, the vibrated concrete column casings were accepted as adding about 28 per cent to their carrying capacity; this was the first time that such a con-

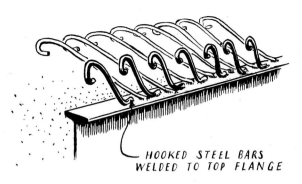

HOOKED STEEL BARS
WELDED TO TOP FLANGE

Fig. A 3, types of anchor used in composite members of steel joists and concrete slabs. Below, system used in Switzerland of angles welded to top flange of joist. Right, system used in a bridge at Melbourne, Australia, of hooked steel bars welded to top flange of joist.

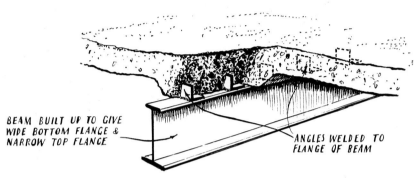

BEAM BUILT UP TO GIVE
WIDE BOTTOM FLANCE &
NARROW TOP FLANCE

ANGLES WELDED TO
FLANGE OF BEAM

cession had been made in England. An equally significant development in combining steel with concrete is the system which involves a compound action between an uncased steel joist and a reinforced concrete slab by means of anchors, welded to the joist and embedded in the slab, which transfer the horizontal shear developed by the composite section. Fig. A.3. shows two types of anchor, one consisting of steel angles and the other of hooked steel bars. This system has been used in a number of structures in Switzerland where it was first introduced in 1914, and appears to have been adopted in a number of other countries including the U. S. A. It seems so far to have been mainly used in bridge construction but it is equally applicable to buildings. The use of floor slabs as compression flanges of beams, particularly if combined with a lighter form of fireproofing, might go a long way towards increasing the efficiency of steel-framed buildings.

Trends

The use of steel has always been firmly established on a scientific basis, since it was not introduced until the mechanical and mathematical sciences had reached a fairly advanced state of development. Its applications have been handicapped, however, by limitations of jointing and manufacture. With improvements in production methods, the development of welding, and the introduction of new alloy steels with special properties, we may see a much greater flexibility in the use of the material.

Increasingly precise knowledge of the characteristics of the material is being obtained but there is a danger of this being confined to independent specialists unless the architect realises the necessity to analyse the complete process of a material's development if he is to make full use of its structural potentialities. This argument can be applied to a certain extent to all structural materials but it is particularly relevant in the case of a factory-made material like steel. At the same time, increased knowledge and the results of research can only be fully utilised in practice, if accompanied by suitable revisions of regulations and methods of design. Such revisions are usually slow to materialise but in the past have resulted in considerable savings of material without in any way reducing the safety of the structures. A new approach is particularly necessary now that structures can be designed as organic entities. The increasing acceptance of continuity in structural design has been accompanied by a great deal of research into the behaviour of such structures, and tests on continuous beams and rigid frames have shown that stresses above the elastic limit in any part of the structure will be absorbed by means of a redistribution of bending moments, having the effect of retarding the failure of the whole structure. This important aspect of continuity was recognised in the revisions to the U. S. Code of Practice made in 1946, which introduced an increase of 20 per cent in the permissible stress at the supports of continuous members.

The fact that continuous structures act as complete units requires from the architect that they be conceived as such. By making such structures practical, and by providing a greater measure of control over the material, welding seems to herald a new freedom in the design of steel structures; at the same time the forms of structural members are likely to be modified if welding becomes widely used, partly to suit the new technique and partly as a result of the greater control over the material.

The necessity for protecting steel against fire and corrosion, and the difficulty of making neat riveted connections, has resulted in comparatively little attention being paid to its appearance, and although there have been examples of the accentuation of rivets as a deliberate element in design, the scope of riveted construction in this respect, has been very limited. Welding, combined with lighter forms of protection, promises to provide greatly improved aesthetic possibilities in the use of steel, not only in the field of structural refinement but possibly also in the suitable emphasis of the rugged texture of the arc weld or the patterning of the spot-weld on a plain metal surface.[30] Finally, an increased knowledge of the way in which steel can be made to co-operate with concrete, may lead towards the design of structures on the basis of combining different materials, each applied in the role which it performs most efficiently.

[30]See Paul Weidlinger "Welding" in Progressive Architecture, July, 1947.

REINFORCED CONCRETE

Historical Note

Although concrete was virtually rediscovered a few years before the completion of the earliest cast-iron bridge towards the end of the eighteenth century,[31] it was more than a hundred years later before concrete, reinforced with steel, was used to any extent in building structures. By that time construction in iron had been highly developed and the early use of reinforced concrete tended to follow the forms perpetuated in early iron construction, with columns, main beams, and secondary beams as principal structural elements. It was soon realised, however, that for the first time a material was available which by its nature invited the conception of a structure as a whole, and not as the sum of its separate parts. The subsequent development of the structural slab and shell was traced in Chapter I.

At the same time, great advances have been made, particularly in recent years, in the quality of both steel and concrete, resulting in corresponding developments in the ways in which they can be combined to form the structure. Moreover, since it is a composite material capable of being moulded in the field according to the requirements of the architect, the latter is concerned equally with methods of obtaining improved quality of materials, and with advances in the manner of combining them in the structure.

Structural Characteristics

The most commonly known characteristic about concrete itself is that it is weak in tension and shear, and without reinforcement can therefore only be used in much the same way as brick or stone. Its most efficient role is, therefore, as a compression member where reinforcement can be kept to a minimum. An important factor, however, is that the rather low modulus of elasticity of concrete does not remain constant and this gives rise to what is called plastic flow or creep, over a period of time. This has an important effect on columns or other compression members where the load is assumed to be distributed between the concrete and compression reinforcement, since steel has a constant modulus of elasticity and, therefore, the manner in which the load is apportioned between steel and concrete may be entirely changed over a period of years. This has led to the development of a new design method based on the ultimate strength of the member, which is assumed to be the sum of the strengths of the steel and concrete considered separately. As yet, however, this method is not universally adopted. This phenomenon shows itself equally in beams where its effect may be noticeable by a gradual increase in deflection.

When used in bending in the customary rectangular form, there is obviously a great deal of concrete below the neutral axis, which, except in so far as it is required for shear, is structurally redundant. This applies equally to beams or to rigid frames where there are large moments to be resisted, and for large members it seems usual to shape the structural element into hollow form (see fig. 60) which means more costly formwork but a saving in material. Alternatively, the application of pre-stressing (see later) permits this material to be brought into active structural use, thereby reducing the required size of the structural member. Pre-stressing may, on the other hand, by increasing the shear strength of the beam, permit the elimination of much of this material by the use of an I-section (see fig. 118). The shaping

---

[31]See "Space, Time and Architecture" page 244.

of the structural members so as to distribute the stresses as evenly as possible, especially by reducing the concentration of stresses caused by bending, is of particular value in reinforced concrete, since lattice forms are costly in formwork and at the same time the dead-weight of the structure must be reduced to a minimum, if it is to be suitable for long spans.

Quality of Materials

When concrete was used without reinforcement, it was customary to employ stiff mixes in thin compacted layers in order to obtain a dense and durable material. With the smaller sections of reinforced concrete, however, it became necessary to use thinner mixes so that the concrete would flow readily around the reinforcement. This often resulted in an inferior material, since concrete only requires sufficient water to hydrate the cement, and any excess merely serves to weaken the finished product by the formation of water voids. The demand for an economical method of placing stiffer mixes has been met by the development of high frequency vibration, applied either to the formwork or direct to the concrete (see fig. A.4.), but even the use of this method requires a mix containing a greater quantity of water than is necessary to hydrate the cement. Recent attention has, therefore, been devoted to the removal of the excess water after the concrete has been placed. One method devised, which is suitable for field-poured concrete, is the use of vacuum mats which will reduce the water content through a thickness of about 12 inches. Since the process is a gentle one, however, the thorough mixing produced by the vibration process is not obtained, and it has therefore been suggested that the two methods might usefully be combined. An alternative method is the use of absorptive form linings such as fibreboard, which were originally introduced to improve the finished appearance of the concrete, but which can remove the excess water for a depth of at least one inch below the surface, producing a greatly improved surface skin of concrete. It is thought better, however, to vibrate concrete cast behind such linings, and by this means a material of very high quality can be obtained. For pre-cast concrete produced in the shop, speed is likely to be of particular importance and attention has therefore been devoted to methods of increasing the rate of hardening of the concrete by taking advantage of the conditions of shop production. The application of heat by steam curing speeds up the hardening of the concrete at the same time as providing the dampness required to prevent cracking. By a combination of vibration, application of high pressure to expel the excess water, and steam curing, concrete can now be produced having very great strength only a few hours after pouring, and an eventual safe working stress much higher than is normally recognised by most building regulations.

The processing required for the production of such high grade material makes it necessary to ensure that its strength should be developed to the maximum in the structural member. Where this is not possible it may be advantageous to combine it with a light weight concrete, made either from a lightweight aggregate or a process of aeration. In exposed situations it may be necessary to retain a dense concrete around the reinforcement, since the lightweight concretes are more porous, but otherwise a combination of dense concrete for the compression area and lightweight concrete for the remainder seems a likely method of increasing efficiency.

The increase in quality of concrete has been accompanied by an equivalent increase in the strength of steel suitable for reinforcement. In addition to ordinary high tensile steel, material of increased strength is obtained by the cold twisting or stretching of mild steel bars. This is done by twisting single bars (see fig. A.5.) or by twisting pairs of bars together; and by stretching small round bars along their length into what is called hard-drawn wire. High tensile wires such as are used for ropes and pianos, are now available up to a strength of 5 or 6 times that of mild steel.

In reinforced concrete members, the basis of co-operation between steel and concrete is the bond which exists between them. In the case of ordinary mild or high tensile steel, the destruction of the bond begins when the yield point of the steel has been reached and the latter may not be much more than a half of the ultimate strength of the material. The cold-twisted or cold-stretched steels, however, have no yield point, and, therefore, a much higher percentage of their ultimate strength can be used. The extent to which it can be developed depends on the ability to control the cracks which occur in the tension zone of the concrete. These must be limited in size in order to protect the steel and their width is largely influenced by the efficiency of the bond. The twisted bars referred to have been found to give an efficient bond up to a certain size of bar, but various types of deformed and indented bars have been developed which provide a more efficient bond and which therefore permit the higher strength of the steel to be developed. Tests have shown that the bond improves as the bearing area of the deformations increases. Deformed bars are familiar in the U. S. A. and the introduction into Sweden of a new type, as a result of wartime steel shortage, was found to show a considerable saving both in quantity of steel and in cost. Nevertheless, even in this special form, the maximum strength of steel which can be used for reinforcing concrete in the con-

Fig. A 4, high frequency vibration applied direct to the concrete: left, before vibration; right, after vibration.

ventional manner is considerably below that of the strongest steels now obtainable, since the use of steel of higher strength would result in larger cracks than are considered desirable.[32]

Fig. A 5, left, twisting of square reinforcing bar increases strength and improves bond with concrete.

The use of the very high strength steels therefore requires a different method of combining the materials, so as to reduce or eliminate the cracking of concrete; the idea that this should be done by using the reinforcement to induce initial compression in the concrete is apparently nearly as old as that of reinforced concrete itself. Early experiments were unsuccessful, however, mainly because plastic flow of concrete had not been discovered and because the steel used was not strong enough to permit initial stressing which could afford the combined loss of pre-stress caused by shrinkage and plastic flow. With present day high strength steel, it is possible to pre-stress to such a degree that a substantial stress remains even after the losses have occurred. Fig. A.6. shows diagrammatically the principle of pre-stressing as applied to a homogeneous section. It amounts to the application of a form of reverse loading which induces compression in that part of the member which is normally in tension under the action of the load. This, as seen in the illustration, results in the setting up of comparatively small tensile stresses in the compression zone of the member; these may be entirely counteracted by the dead weight of the member itself or can be provided for by reinforcement. The important point, however, is that when bending takes place due to loading, the whole of the compression force in the tension zone must be overcome before the concrete itself will be in tension. By suitably choosing the amount of pre-stressing and position of the stretched reinforcement, the stress distribution under loading can be varied within wide limits but is normally designed to produce no tension in the concrete. By this means cracking can be controlled and the highest strength steel can therefore be used. In addition, the initial tension in the compression zone reduces the eventual stress in the concrete, and this, combined with the stressing of the whole concrete section, leads to a reduction in the size of the structural member. Where dead load is an important part of the whole, such as in bridges, the overall saving in weight of concrete may amount to as much as 70 per cent compared with normal reinforced concrete, and the amount of steel required may be as little as 15 per cent of that required for the conventional method of reinforcing.

[32]See Dr. K. Hajnal-Konyi "Concrete" in "New Ways of Building" edited by E. de Mare (The Architectural Press, London).

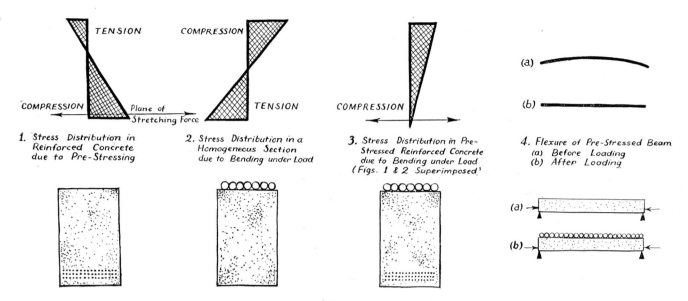

1. Stress Distribution in Reinforced Concrete due to Pre-Stressing

2. Stress Distribution in a Homogeneous Section due to Bending under Load

3. Stress Distribution in Pre-Stressed Reinforced Concrete due to Bending under Load (Figs. 1 & 2 Superimposed)

4. Flexure of Pre-Stressed Beam
   (a) Before Loading
   (b) After Loading

Fig. A 6, above, diagrammatic representation of the principle of pre-stressing.

Various systems have been devised for applying the initial tension to the reinforcement, either before or after the casting of the concrete. Pre-tensioning, in which the concrete is poured around the stretched reinforcement, relies on the bond between the steel and concrete for its effectiveness and normally makes use of a large number of fine wires which have a high ratio of surface to cross-sectional area and become wedged at the ends when the tension is released. Post-tensioning involves the prevention of bond between the wires and the concrete, either by sheathing or suitable coating, and subsequent stretching of the reinforcement after the concrete has hardened: this may be done by means of jacks, one type of which is shown in fig. A.7., and is has also been attempted by heating the wires by means of an electric current. Expanding cements are also being developed, by means of which the same principle can be applied; in this case, the concrete is the active part inducing preliminary stress by means of bond as it tries to expand. The quality at present manufactured, however, apparently does not produce an induced stress comparable to that which is desirable or possible by using the steel as the active agent.[33] If it can be improved it may provide certain advantages over the mechanical stretching of the steel, the apparatus for which, tends to limit the application of the system. Post-tensioning is normally required for field-poured work, pre-tensioning being used for pre-cast members produced in the shop where anchorage and equipment can be more readily made available.

Pre-stressing improves the efficiency not only of members in bending, but also of those in direct tension, such as occur in lattice girders, since high strength steel can be used having a concrete protection in which all cracks can be eliminated. The efficiency of compression members can also be improved, however, by containing the concrete in a steel enclosure which has the effect of compensating for the lack of cohesion in the concrete, and thereby increasing the stresses which it can sustain. The most widely used method is that of helical binding, by means of which the strength of the concrete is increased as the spacing of consecutive spiral bands becomes closer. The ultimate development is the steel tube, and in such a

[33]See K. Billig "Prestressed Reinforced Concrete"—paper read to the Reinforced Concrete Association, London, October, 1946.

case the concrete could, in theory, become completely plastic, like liquid in a piston, with the strength of the member dependent only on the steel.[34] A system of injecting concrete under pressure into thin steel tubes has been used both in France and in the U. S. A. The pressure creates an initial tension in the tube and bond is thereby maintained, in spite of shrinkage of the concrete. Greatly increased strength is obtainable by this means, compared with concrete reinforced in the normal way.

These developments in the methods of combining the basic materials of reinforced concrete are beginning to have repercussions on the forms of the members themselves, which are tending to hollow out into the familiar shapes of rolled steel, by virtue of the higher grade material and the reduced size of reinforcement. At the same time the high degree of control and expensive equipment favours shop production and has brought about a great advance in the manufacture of pre-cast products, although the idea of pre-casting is nearly as old as the material itself. In the U. S. A. standard structural members have been developed which can be selected from tables in the same way as for structural steel (see fig. 6). Pre-casting combined with pre-stressing also encourages the use of lattice members, which can be delivered in sections and assembled in the field (see fig. 28).

Fig. A 7, type of pre-stressing jack developed by E. Freyssinet and operated by compressed air. Pre-stressing wires are grouped into a series of cables, each group being stretched in one operation.

Jointing and Assembly

It is only with the development of pre-casting that the problem of jointing has entered into the field of reinforced concrete. Its implications were discussed earlier in Chapter I and the main object of the joint, whether in built-up members or in the assembly of the structure itself, is normally to attain the same degree of continuity as would be possessed if the structure was poured in the field. Where jointing is carried out at zones of minimum stress, bolting is sometimes used; where the joint itself has to resist high stresses, however, it may be made either by means of steel connectors rigidly anchored into the members to be spliced, or by welding corresponding reinforcing bars, and completing in both cases with concrete casing.

[34]See A. Hermant and L. Bourgine "Structures et Formes en Beton Armé", in Techniques et Architecture, (France) January/February, 1944.

Alternatively, poured-in-place joints may be made with suitable splicing bars and adequate preparation of the concrete surfaces to be joined.[35]

Durability

Since concrete is used for the protection of steel from corrosion and fire, reinforced concrete is clearly satisfactory from these points of view provided sufficient cover is given to the reinforcement. This is particularly necessary for external work where inadequate cover may result in spalling of the concrete and subsequent deterioration of the steel reinforcement.

Developments in Application

The freedom of design with reinforced concrete is brought about only by means of costly form-work. If economy in formwork is to be obtained, then some of this freedom must be given up for the sake of standardisation. Recommendations have been made in England that dimensions of structural members should be standardised to permit the use of pre-fabricated forms in different combinations, and that their strength should be varied by the design of the mix and percentage of reinforcement. The assumption was, that even if this meant using more concrete, there would be an overall saving resulting from economy in form-work and speed of erection. There remains, however, the cost of erecting the formwork and only precasting, with its attendant problems of jointing, can overcome this. The pre-casting of heavy units in the shop, however, also creates problems of transport and handling and this seems to have led to an increasing use of pre-casting in the field. The use of this method for heavy members, combined with shop production of light units, is said to be one of the main reasons for the great development of the pre-cast industry in the U.S.S.R.[36] A useful compromise seems to be the use of pre-cast units as permanent form-work, designed to carry dead loads until the poured-in-place concrete comes into operation to assist in carrying the full loads. This method has been used in Switzerland both for floors and for bridges, employing pre-cast units which are also pre-stressed, and it appears to have considerable possibilities in applying the advantages of pre-stressing and pre-casting in an economical way. Joints in this method can become part of the poured-in-place concrete.

In general, developments in the application and usefulness of reinforced concrete as a structural material seem to depend very much on the economic aspect of pre-stressing, which is largely influenced by the cost ratio between labour and material. This may affect the degree to which the potentialities of pre-stressing in creating lighter, more resilient and more durable structures in reinforced concrete can be exploited in any given place or country.

Trends

It was reinforced concrete which pointed the way to new structural forms and by its nature it remains for the architect the most easily moulded material. Its principal disadvantage is the costly form-work required for using its great potentialities and it was perhaps this fact which made steel the more popular material during the first quarter of the century. The forms of the material are, therefore, likely to be governed to some extent by economical methods of providing temporary support, and in this respect the use of flexible fabrics, which serve at the same time to introduce a shape of inherent structural rigidity, is noteworthy. Pre-casting still remains a low percentage of the volume of work carried out and introduces limitations

[35]See K. Billig "Structural Precast Reinforced Concrete" — paper read to the Institution of Civil Engineers, London, March, 1947.

[36]See K. Billig "Structural Precast Reinforced Concrete"—reference above.

similar to those of steel, but the use of thin pre-cast units to provide temporary support in place of steel or timber, and forming part of the finished monolithic structure, seems a most likely development. Increasing knowledge of the materials, such as the plastic flow or yield of the concrete under sustained loading, which affects the way in which the steel and concrete co-operate, is leading to gradual revision of design methods which differ very widely at present from one country to another. For instance, a column with helical binding designed in accordance with U. S. regulations requires twice as much concrete and one and a half times as much steel as a similar column designed for Brazilian regulations, mainly as a result of a difference in permissible stresses.[37] This explains the greater slenderness of reinforced concrete buildings in South America. Greater control over the material means greater aesthetic possibilities in structural refinement, and this is assisted by improvement in the proportions of structural members resulting from pre-stressing. Above all, reinforced concrete requires early collaboration between architect, engineer and contractor if the best results are to be obtained and the potentialities of the material are to be fully exploited.

[37]See A. J. Boase "South American Structures" Part III in Engineering News-Record, June 28th, 1945.

TIMBER

Timber is not only the oldest of the tensile structural materials but is unique in the fact that it is produced by nature with its structural potential ready for use and not requiring the complex manufacturing processes such as are needed for the production of the more recent structural materials. Moreover, the growth of timber has stood for all time as one of nature's remarkable lessons of the principle of structural continuity, and in the earliest times the natural curved shapes of the material as it grew in the tree were sometimes used in their crude form in the way in which we would now use rigid frames. The dissection and conversion of the tree into small pieces of timber more adaptable to building requirements breaks up a continuous structure in which the strength of the material is efficiently distributed to perform its natural function; it therefore produces a material of variable quality depending on the part of the tree from which it comes. For many centuries, however, there was no theoretical knowledge on which design could be based, so that the technique of timber construction grew up largely on the basis of trial and error into quite a highly developed art but with no theory to support it. It therefore became so established as the material of the craftsman, that even when structural science was developed, it was not applied to timber but awaited the appearance of steel and reinforced concrete, which by their nature were more suitable for the application of mathematical theory, and were therefore developed on a scientific basis right from the start.[38] It is only in recent years, therefore, that timber has received the scientific attention denied to it for so long, and we are faced with the paradox that although it is the oldest of all the structural materials capable of being used in tension or bending, it is one of the newest in potentiality. A contributory factor is that plastics, although at present unsuitable for use as structural materials by themselves, are able, in the form of synthetic resins, to assist greatly towards increasing the structural value of timber.

Timber is an organic material with two main constituents, one of which provides its strength in tension and the other its strength in compression. Its strength varies in different planes, the maximum strength being in the direction of the grain, and although traditional practice was, as far as possible, to avoid using it in direct tension, this appears to have been due to the difficulty of making satisfactory tension joints, and timber is actually stronger in tension than in compression. Weakness in shear in the direction of the grain is one of the main factors which, until recent developments, made satisfactory tension joints difficult to obtain.

At the same time, timber is a material of fairly low density which means that its constituents are more extensively distributed than those of a dense material such as steel, and it therefore possesses a greater degree of flexural rigidity, weight for weight. This also results, of course, in larger sectional areas for given loading, but so long as this is acceptable, timber becomes comparatively more efficient for structural members which are likely to fail through elastic instability before being able to develop their proper strength; or for members whose deflection must be strictly limited. Members in compression or bending are the ones concerned, especially

[38]See Philip O. Reece "Recent Experience in the Design of Timber Structures" in the Journal of the Royal Institute of British Architects, March, 1944.

where the load is light compared with the length of the member or where slenderness is particularly great such as in the stressing of sheet material in its own plane. Timber also has the ability to resist, over short periods, loads considerably in excess of those which it will support under sustained loading. This applies for instance to wind-pressure and impact loading, and in this respect it compares favorably with other materials.

**Quality
of
Materials**

Timber, being a product of nature, is subject to a varying range of characteristics which may affect its strength, such as moisture content or the visible characteristics of knots, shakes, rate of growth, etc. In order that structural theory may be applied to it, however, there must be some method of grading its mechanical properties. In practice this is done by the measurement of the various defects of the timber in relation to its dimensions, and also by recording the characteristics of its growth. By this means safe working stresses may be assigned to timber pieces for specific structural purposes, and this is known as stress grading.

This system of classifying the strength of timber can only give fairly approximate results, and within any particular category there is bound to remain quite a difference in strength between timbers selected at random. There is a tendency, however, for the strength of most specimens to approximate to a mean value between the strongest and the weakest,[39] whereas the safe working stress for single members of the particular grade is bound to be based upon the specimen of least strength. It is clear, therefore, that efficiency of timber can be increased by combining two or more graded members into a single unit, since the average strength of the composite member is bound to be greater than that of the weakest member of the grade. This forms the basis of lamination, and so long as the laminae are securely united, the working stresses of laminated members can be justifiably increased. By statistical analysis of test specimens the permissible increases have been established according to the number of laminations. In order to take advantage of this increased strength, however, members used in bending must clearly have the laminae parallel to the plane of bending, otherwise the strength would still depend on that of the layers at the extremities, which have to sustain the maximum stresses. At the same time it is possible to build up material with the layers perpendicular to the plane of bending, by making the outer laminae of high-grade timber to take the maximum stresses, with lower grade material forming the lightly stressed portion of the member.

The normal method of lamination combines timbers of substantial thickness with their grains roughly parallel (see fig. A. 8.) and in this form the material retains its disadvantages of shrinkage and structural weakness at right angles to the grain. In the case of plywood, however, which is a special form of lamination, the alternation of the direction of the grain in successive plies provides high strength in both directions, and at the same time moisture movement is restrained by the tendency of alternate plies to shrink in different directions. Plywood is therefore timber's equivalent of the thin concrete slab reinforced in two directions.

**Structural
Members**

The principle of lamination provides much greater freedom in converting the tree into suitable structural members. These are no longer limited to the maximum size that can be cut from the tree, nor are they limited in shape by the way in

[39]See Philip O. Reece "Timber" in "New Ways of Building"—reference above.

214

Fig. A 8, glued laminated dredge spuds for U. S. Army Engineers approximately 2 ft. square and 55 ft. long.

which the tree grows, or by the way in which the timber can be economically cut. This fact, together with the development of new adhesives and new methods of mechanical jointing, has opened up fresh fields of potential structural members, which were previously limited to the straight pieces cut from the tree or to small built-up sections greatly handicapped by problems of jointing. The two main types of member are those of lattice form, and those of closed type which may be either solid or hollowed out into box or I-section. Various examples were shown in Chapter I. Laminated members are particularly suitable for rigid frame or other continuous forms of construction where the section of the member and grade of material can be varied according to the stress distribution. Laminated members are equally useful, however, in providing chords sufficiently large to enable lattice girders of very considerable span to be constructed. Plywood can perform the same function as thin steel plate in the formation of plate girders, or in taking shear stress in any other form of built-up member. With suitable stiffening it can be used as a stressed skin taking direct forces in its own plane and it seems that it may have possibilities in this field in the future.

Problems of jointing seem to have been the main retarding influence on the development of the structural potential of timber, for even without the knowledge of structural theory, it is certain that the craftsman would have displayed his skill in more daring timber structures if suitable methods of jointing had been available. The two main advances have been in the development of stronger and more durable

Jointing and Assembly

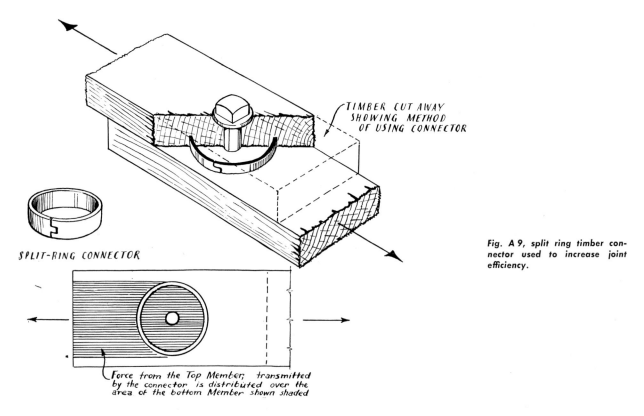

TIMBER CUT AWAY
SHOWING METHOD
OF USING CONNECTOR

SPLIT-RING CONNECTOR

Fig. A 9, split ring timber connector used to increase joint efficiency.

Force from the Top Member, transmitted by the connector is distributed over the area of the bottom Member shown shaded

glues and in the improvement of methods of mechanical jointing.

Although glues have been known and used since early times, it is only in recent years that glues have been developed which not only have very great strength, but are durable and water-resistant. It is in this field that plastics are contributing to structural development, in the form of synthetic resins which are the glues which combine these properties. The main application seems to be in the building up of laminated material or of completely laminated members, and since plywood is dependent upon gluing, synthetic resins contribute greatly to its wider structural application. The gluing of timber is comparable to the welding of steel, in that it permits joints to be made without cutting any material out of the members joined and makes it possible to obtain the advantages of structural continuity. At the same time some of these adhesives require the controlled conditions of the shop for their application and this may tend to limit the application of gluing in the field.

For field connections mechanical joints, equivalent to riveting or bolting in steel-work, seem likely to predominate. Although laminated members can be built up by means of bolting or nailing, they lend themselves particularly to gluing when they can be shop produced, but they may be so large as to require field assembly, for which mechanical joints are normally used. It is in the field of framed lattice structures, however, that the mechanical joint has assumed special importance since they were limited in their development until the problem of the tension joint could be solved, especially while reliable glues were still not available. As a result of research into this problem in the last few decades, various forms of mechanical joint have been developed, all based on the same principle. One of the most widely used is the split ring timber connector shown in fig. A. 9. The split in the ring enables it to open slightly under load, so that both the inside and the outside bear against the timber and transmit the forces over the area shown shaded in the illustration. By this means a much greater distribution area is obtained than with a bolt used alone, and the strength of the joint is therefore increased. In general these forms of connection must be regarded as pin-joints, but where more than one connector is used, a certain degree of rigidity is likely to be introduced. Timber connectors, which made possible the construction of the blimp hangars shown in fig. 48, are also assisting in improving the efficiency of small scale timber construction such as roof trusses for domestic purposes.

Timber is subject to the disadvantages of high inflammability, deterioration under sustained exposure to moisture and the elements, and liability to attack by vermin and wood destroying fungi. So long as it was the only material which could be used in bending, these limitations had to be accepted and durability was very dependent upon vigilance and maintenance. Fire hazard can now be much reduced by the use of special surface paints or impregnation with fire-retardant chemicals, and these treatments have not been found to cause any reduction in the strength of the material. Similarly, wood-preservatives are now available to protect the timber from moisture and from vermin, and the waterproof glues are apparently unaffected by most of these treatments. Attack by wood destroying fungi can be avoided by using the timber in accordance with present-day knowledge, so that a scientific use of the material combined with the preservative treatments available makes timber potentially much more durable than it was in the past.

Durability

Timber has become one of the recognised engineering materials, and can now be used as scientifically as any other. Developments in its application seem to have been mainly in large span single-storey structures and in increasing its efficiency in its traditional forms; large span bridges have also been constructed. It is in structures of this kind that timber seems most likely to be employed, since its bulk makes it normally unsuitable for multi-storey construction, and special precautions must be taken to reduce the fire hazard. Lamination creates a tendency towards shop assembly of the structural members and greatly increases the architectural potentialities of timber, making it suitable for many types of single-storey structure where it might not have been considered before. Plywood, the special type of laminated timber, is particularly suited for stressed skin construction, which, being so light, is of special value in the design of prefabricated units. As in the case of steel, therefore, timber has developed well beyond its early use in the essentially one-dimensional form.

Developments in Application

Although considerable advances in timber construction were made between the wars, probably the most significant developments took place in the United States during World War II as a result of the shortage of steel in the presence of an abundant timber supply. Laminated construction had been developed and successfully used in Europe before its adoption in the U.S.A., but as one might expect, it was mainly confined to the timber producing countries. In Switzerland, as in the U.S.A., an impetus was given to timber construction by the shortage of steel during the war years, and laminated timber structures were used where steel or reinforced concrete would normally have been employed.

The greater use of laminated timber has come at a time when increasing attention is being given to continuous structures in the form of rigid arches and frames, and timber is now a suitable medium for the expression of stress distribution in the purity of structural form. For the first time, therefore, since trees were used in their

Trends

natural forms as means of support, timber is being converted from its natural form in the tree, into forms based on nature's principle of continuity but satisfying the requirements of man. In short, it is becoming a freer structural medium responding more easily to the architect's creative vision and no longer restricted by the weaknesses which resulted from the dissection of the tree—an organic structure—into many small pieces of varying quality and limited shape and size. Although the development of timber structures employing the new techniques is likely to be limited in the early stages to countries having a large native supply of the raw material, the architectural possibilities imparted to the material cannot fail to arouse universal interest.

ALUMINIUM ALLOYS

Historical
Note

Non-ferrous metals are the youngest of the structural materials and have as yet been comparatively little used. Although magnesium alloys are thought to be of possible structural value and were produced in increased quantities during World War II, it is the aluminium alloys which are at present significant in the structural field. Aluminium itself was apparently produced nearly a hundred years ago, but its strength was not very great and it was only with the development of the alloy Duralumin, in the early part of the century, that a metal was obtained with a strength suitable for structural purposes. This name was subsequently adopted for a whole range of alloys of similar composition. Developments in the last quarter of a century have produced a greatly improved range of aluminium alloys having ultimate tensile strengths of up to 35-40 tons per square inch. They vary considerably in their suitability for different purposes and also in the methods by which they can be fabricated.

Structural
Characteristics

Most alloys of the duralumin group have approximately the same strength in tension and compression as steel, and a weight which is only slightly more than one third that of the latter. The advantage of this high strength/weight ratio, however, is liable to be offset by their low modulus of elasticity (about one third that of steel). This means that for members of similar dimensions, the aluminium alloys are lower in flexural rigidity than steel, and the shape and proportions of the structural member therefore become all important factors. For instance, where deflection must be kept to a minimum to avoid cracking of ceiling plaster, an aluminium alloy section may need to be rather deeper than an equivalent steel beam. Continuity in construction, therefore becomes even more important in the case of aluminium than with steel, for complete continuity produces only one fifth of the deflection which would be obtained with a freely supported beam. Similarly, in the design of compression members, the disposition of material to provide a maximum and uniform flexural rigidity becomes particularly important. The disadvantage is that the hollow section, which can provide the most efficient shape, will also tend to occupy a greater floor space. Local instability is also of added importance owing to the elasticity of the material, and this will affect the form of the structural member which may require local stiffening in much the same way as is required in steel shapes formed of light-gauge sheet material. On the other hand, the low modulus of elasticity results in a reasonably good ability to absorb energy within the elastic range, so that aluminium alloys are advantageous for withstanding impact loads.

Thermal expansion of aluminium alloys is about twice that of steel, so that for certain structural applications the effects of temperature change will require rather more consideration than is usual with the latter.[40]

Structural
Members

Aluminium alloys are of two distinct types: the non-heat-treatable, and the heat-treatable produced by heating and quenching. The former range from low to medium strength, have a high ductility, and are capable of being welded; those in the latter group, which includes the duralumins, are of high strength and are there-

[40]See D. V. Pike "The Application of Light Aluminium Alloys to Structural Engineering", in "The Structural Engineer," (London) July, 1945.

fore most suitable for structural purposes, but they have less ductility and are unsuitable for welding, since they lose some of their strength when heated. Alloys of aluminium may be obtained in the form of castings or of wrought metal but it is the latter which lend themselves more to structural work. Wrought alloys are formed into suitable structural shapes by extrusion, drawing or rolling, but extrusion is the most flexible process. A single section of complex shape can be extruded in aluminium alloy, where a compound member of several sections, riveted or welded together, would be required with rolled sections in steel. This means that the shape can be more readily designed for maximum structural efficiency, and even where this involves departure from standard sections, it may be found economical as a result of the saving in material. It is worth noting in this connection, that developments have taken place in recent years in the forming of structural shapes from sheet material; this parallels the similar tendency referred to in the case of steel.

Jointing and Assembly

The necessity for jointing in the building up of individual members should be reduced by the ability to extrude complex sections as single units. The jointing of one member to another, however, presents the same problem as accompanies construction in steel, with the disadvantage that the heat-treatable alloys most suitable for structural purposes owing to their strength, are at the same time unsuitable for welding, as was mentioned above. At the present time, therefore, it seems that riveting or bolting must generally be used in the case of the high strength alloys where the full strength of the material must be maintained. There are, however, non-heat-treatable alloys of lower strength which may be found suitable for structural work in cases for instance where high resistance to corrosion is a particular asset, and these alloys can be welded by all the normal processes.

Durability

The resistance of most aluminium alloys to atmospheric attack under normal urban and rural conditions is greatly superior to that of most other metals, as is shown by the comparative corrosion of metals exposed for seven years to a typical industrial atmosphere (fig. A.10.). This is mainly due to the thin but impervious film of oxide which forms on the surface of the metal when it is exposed to the air and which re-forms immediately if removed. In special cases, however, such as exposure to marine atmosphere, care is necessary in choosing the most suitable alloy for maximum resistance to corrosion. The maximum degree of resistance combined with high mechanical strength can be provided by cladding a duralumin with pure aluminium.

In spite of the high corrosion resistance of aluminium alloys, painting is considered desirable in most cases where the metal is exposed externally,[41] but it may not always be essential where non-heat-treatable alloys are used. Particular care is necessary where the material is in close proximity to other metals, since aluminium is liable to electrolytic corrosion when in contact with most other metals in the presence of moisture. Contact with building materials may also promote corrosion, especially if they contain alkalis in the presence of moisture, as, for instance, in the case of damp concrete or plaster.[42] In general, protection against the effects of this corrosion can be provided by means of asphaltic or bituminous coverings.

It would seem, at first sight, that the comparatively low melting point of aluminium alloys would produce a greater fire risk—i.e. a shorter period of structural stability

[41]See R. L. Moore "How and When to Use Aluminium Alloys" in Engineering News-Record, Oct. 18th, 1945.
[42]See D. V. Pike—reference above.

under the effects of heat—than is the case with steel. However, certain claims have been made to the contrary on the basis of the higher conductivity of the material, but research has evidently not yet provided a conclusive answer. The most one can say, is that the great difference in strength-reducing temperatures between steel and duralumin is not necessarily indicative of a corresponding difference in the period of fire-resisting stability of structures composed of these materials.

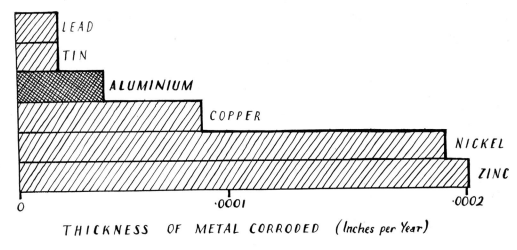

THICKNESS OF METAL CORRODED (Inches per Year)

Fig. A 10, above, comparative corrosion of metals exposed to the atmosphere for seven years at Birmingham, England. (Investigations by Dr. J. Newton Friend.)

Applications

Although the aluminium alloys might be suitable as materials for a large variety of structures, the fact that their cost is at present high compared with that of steel makes it necessary to seek those applications in which their assets of high strength/weight ratio and good resistance to corrosion are of maximum value.

It seems that the weight of a structure designed with aluminium alloys may be reduced to roughly two-fifths of that of an equivalent steel structure, where there are no special limitations with regard to the depth or width of structural members. Although this saving in weight may not always be sufficient to reduce the sizes of the members used, it can be particularly important in structures having substantial dead loads. In long spans, for instance, the weight of the structure itself creates a large percentage of the total stresses, so that the advantage of weight-saving provided by the aluminium alloys, becomes more marked as the span increases, so long as deflection is not limited. This fact was well demonstrated in the case of the 360 ft. span Smithfield Street suspension bridge in Pittsburgh, where the replacement of the existing steel and timber roadway by beams and decking of aluminium alloy, produced a dead-weight reduction of about one ton per foot run, and roughly halved the total weight of the roadway. In this way, the bridge was made safe for the greatly increased traffic, at a cost which was about 25 per cent of that of a new steel bridge designed for the same loading.

The first complete bridge span built entirely of aluminium alloy was apparently that constructed in 1946 at Massena, New York (fig. A.11.). With a span of 100 feet, its weight was only just over two-fifths that of the equivalent neighbouring spans in steel. Two years later a complete bascule-type bridge of aluminium alloy was constructed at the port of Sunderland, England (fig. A.12.). The span between

Fig. A 11, left, first complete bridge span of aluminium alloy—one of the 100 ft. spans of the railroad bridge of Massena, New York. (Engineers: Aluminum Company of America; Consultants: Hardesty and Hanover.)

trunnion bearings is about 120 ft. and the weight is again about two-fifths that of an equivalent steel structure. In this instance, the reduced weight is of added advantage since the leaves of the bridge have to be moved up and down. Because of the light weight of the structure it was possible to transport it in large sections as seen in the illustration.

Bridges are of course extreme cases where the dead load assumes maximum importance but some of the problems encountered in buildings seem likely to derive equal benefit from the light-weight of aluminum alloys. A case in point was the construction of a penthouse of aluminium alloy on the roof of an existing foundry building in Canada. The low weight of the structure enabled the original building to withstand the additional loading without any adjustment to the existing frame or foundations. Even from the point of view of erection, there may be some advantage, in certain cases, of having a lighter material for use in the upper storeys of high buildings. Trusses of fairly large span, such as that in fig. A. 13, may also be found advantageous, especially for light loading, but there seems to be considerable scope for the use of appropriate extruded sections combined with more efficient joints, in place of the mere imitation of design in steel. Transport is another factor which may influence the use of aluminium alloys in building, and in remote places this might be an overriding consideration. One example is the refuge at the summit of Mont Blanc, France, where all materials had to be carried up by hand and aluminium was an obvious choice. Portable frames present another instance where lightness is an all-important factor and frames of this sort in aluminium alloy have apparently been used in Germany up to a span of 150 feet. Fig. A.14. shows a transportable single storey structure of aluminium alloy developed in England for such temporary uses as exhibitions. The high strength/weight ratio of the material may also be of value in prefabrication and might open the way to original methods of

Fig. A 12, right and above, bascule type bridge at Sunderland, England, constructed entirely of aluminium alloy. Span 120 ft. between trunnion bearings. (Engineer: F. J. Walker.)

construction, involving the raising of large building units after assembly at ground level.

The reduced maintenance required for aluminium alloys may be an influential factor in the case of high buildings of large floor area, where erection of scaffolding for repainting is considered to be undesirable.[43] Their choice may be even more natural, however, where corrosion is a serious factor such as in railway stations etc. In fact the first structural use of aluminium alloys in the U. S. A. was in the Botanical Gardens, Washington D. C. (fig. A.15.) where the material was employed to resist the corrosive action of high temperature and humidity, and thereby reduce maintenance costs.

Trends

The possibilities of using high strength aluminium alloys for structural purposes have been studied for some years, more particularly it appears in the U. S. A., France and Germany where they have been applied in various ways. Although the needs of the aircraft industry during World War II interrupted these developments, there has been a large increase in the world production of aluminium, accompanied by a corresponding increase in manufacturing capacity of high strength aluminium alloys. Their cost, however, is still high compared with that of steel although price reorientation has moved in favour of aluminium. The high cost appears to be mainly due to the heavy electrical power consumption required for separating aluminium from the raw material alumina. The latter is normally extracted from bauxite but a process is apparently being started in the U. S. A. to extract it from clay. The production of aluminium from clay, if accompanied by the eventual development of cheap atomic power, might well have strong repercussions in the structural field.

At present the principal use of the material seems likely to be in single-storey structures of large span but its use in multi-storey buildings cannot be ruled out.

[43]See Dr. E. C. West "Aluminium Alloys: Some Possible Applications in Building", paper read to the Incorporated Association of Architects and Surveyors, England, June 14th, 1944.

Fig. A 13, right, roof trusses of aluminium alloy having a clear span of 68 ft. (Engineers: Structural and Mechanical Development Engineers, Ltd.)

Fig. A 14, right, transportable structure in aluminium alloy developed in England for temporary use. (Engineers: Structural and Mechanical Development Engineers, Ltd.)

Fig. A 15, above, conservatory framework, Botanical Garden, Washington, D.C. constructed of aluminium alloy to resist corrosive action of high temperature and humidity.

The structural proportions and forms are likely to have their own character when the material is fully developed, owing particularly to its great elasticity, and the trend will probably be away from the standard shapes to which we have become accustomed in steel. It should be noted also, that for very heavy framed construction, steel seems likely to remain the most suitable material for reasons of bulk and the problems of secondary stability connected with large structural members. In general, it appears probable that aluminium alloys will be used in conjunction with other materials in order that the maximum economy should be gained in the structure as a whole. As yet, however, the application of the alloys of aluminium to the solution of contemporary structural problems is still in its very early stages.

Bibliography

The subject of this book embraces such a wide field that no attempt can be made to compile a bibliography which could be regarded in any way as comprehensive. It is felt, however, that the following list may be of value to the reader wishing to pursue some particular aspect of the subject, or requiring further information about any of the structures illustrated. Many of the references contain further bibliographies of a more specialised nature.

GENERAL

Space, Time & Architecture—Sigfried Giedion (Harvard University Press, 1941)

The New Architecture—A. Roth (Verlag für Architecktur A. G., Erlenbach-Zürich, 1946)

Robert Maillart—Max Bill (Verlag für Architektur A. G., Erlenbach-Zürich, 1949)

In the Nature of Materials (The buildings of Frank Lloyd Wright)—Henry Russell Hitchcock (Duell, Sloan & Pearce, Inc., New York, 1942)

Le Corbusier et Pierre Jeanneret, Oeuvre Complète 1929/1934 Vol. II (Verlag für Architektur A. G., Erlenbach-Zürich, 1934)

Architectural Construction—Theodore Crane (John Wiley & Sons Inc., New York; Chapman & Hall Ltd., London, 1947)

The Skyscraper—W. C. Clark and J. L. Kingston (Published by American Institute of Steel Construction Inc., 1930)

Brazil—("Architectural Forum", November 1947)

The Influence of New Developments in Construction on Architectural Design—M. Hartland Thomas ("Journal of the Royal Institute of British Architects", March 1944)

A Report on Structural Engineering in Germany—John Mason ("The Structural Engineer", London, June 1946)

Effective Teamwork in Building Design—T. H. Creighton & F. N. Severud ("Engineering News-Record", October 19th 1944)

Efficiency in Structure Invokes the Principle of Continuity—F. N. Severud ("Architectural Record", January 1946)

These War Buildings Were Significant—("Engineering News-Record", October 19th 1944)

Continuity in Construction—Dr. K. Hajnal-Kónyi ("Architects' Journal", London, July 1st, July 8th and September 2nd 1943)

Hangars Analysed—F. N. Severud ("Architectural Record", April 1947)

Post-War Building Techniques ("Architectural Forum", January 1945)

Structures et Formes en Béton Armé—A. Hermant & L. Bourgine ("Techniques et Architecture", Paris, January/February 1944)

Memorandum on Box Frame Construction—Ove Arup (Published privately, London, May 1944)

Box Frame Construction—Ove Arup ("Architects' Journal", London, June 14th, 1945)

Efficiency in Storage and Service—Dr. L. Parnes ("Architectural Record", February 1947)

Tension-structure ("Bollettino Tecnico Savigliano", Turin, April 1932)

Edificio Para Oficinas ("Revista Arquitectura" Buenos Aires, May 1948)

The Design of Rockefeller City—Raymond Hood ("Architectural Forum", January 1932)

Case Study House No. 8 ("Arts and Architecture", December 1945)

Laboratory Tower at Racine; Sports Club in Hollywood Hills ("Architectural Forum", January 1948)

Flats in Palace Gate, Kensington ("Architectural Review", London, April 1939)

De La Warr Pavilion, Bexhill ("Architects' Journal", December 12th 1935)

An Exhibition Hall at Turin, Italy ("La Technique des Travaux", Belgium, September/October 1949)

Ruth Lucie Stern Research Building, San Francisco ("Architectural Record", July 1941)

Health Centre for the Borough of Finsbury ("Architectural Review", London, January 1939)

New Premises for Peter Jones, London ("Architects' Journal", July 9th 1936)

STEEL

Cast-Iron in Building—Richard Sheppard (George Allen & Unwin, London, 1946)

Steel—O. Bondy ("New Ways of Building", The Architectural Press, London, 1948)

Welded Steel Structures—a Survey of Welding in Structural Work (Broadway Advertising Service, London, 1940)

Developments in Welded Steel Construction—La Motte Grover ("Engineering News-Record", October 18th 1945)

Welding—Paul Weidlinger ("Progressive Architecture", July 1947)

Welding—F. J. Samuely ("Architect and Building News", London, July 3rd 1942)

Recent Experience in the Design of Welded Frames—A. Ramsay Moon ("Journal of the Royal Institute of British Architects", May 1944)

War-time Advances in Welding ("Architectural Record", July 1946)

Matériaux et Techniques ("Architecture d'Aujourd'hui", France, March/April 1946)

Steel Design Trends—Dr. M. Salvadori and B. Funaro ("Architectural Record", April 1940)

Light-Gauge Steel for Peacetime Building—Milton Male ("Engineering News-Record", October 18th 1945)

The Rational Design of Steel Building Frames—Prof. J. F. Baker ("Journal of the Institution of Civil Engineers", London, April 21st 1936)

U. S. Steel Building Code Changes Analysed—T. R. Higgins ("Engineering News-Record", October 17th 1946)

Economics of Steel Roofing—S. McConnel ("Civil Engineering", London, May 1945)

Composite Beams—Dr. M. Ross and A. Albrecht ("Bauwesen und Gewerbe", Zürich, Bericht No. 149, March 1944)

Composite Action—letter by W. A. Ozanne ("Engineering News-Record", October 5th 1944)

The Design and Applications of the Vierendeel Truss—P. C. G. Hausser (International Congress for Steel Development)

Flats at Drancy, France—E. Mopin ("The Welder", London, November 1935)

Flats at Leeds, England—E. Mopin ("The Structural Engineer", London, December 1936)

Welded Rigid Frame Factory Building—O. Bondy ("Engineering", London, October 11th and 25th, 1940)

Indoor Stadium Has 222 ft. Rigid Frames—G. W. Holcomb ("Engineering News-Record", August 11th 1949)

Welded Frame for a 16-Storey Building—A. E. Poole and L. F. Booth ("Engineering News-Record", October 31st 1946)

Article on U. S. Navy's Steel Blimp Hangar—A. Amirikian ("Welding Journal", July 1949)

Volière pour Oiseaux, Rome ("L'Ossature Metallique", Brussels, April 1947)

Three Immense Auto Assembly Plants ("Engineering News-Record", October 31st 1946)

Earls Court Exhibition ("Architects' Journal", London, February 3rd 1938; "Architectural Review", London, October 1937)

Economical Factory Construction (in Sheet Steel) ("Building", London, November 1937)

Structural Analysis: No. 26 Piccadilly, London ("Architects' Journal", London, May 21st 1936)

The Murex Works ("The Welder", London, March, October and December 1938; April/June 1949)

New Steel Plant at Port Talbot ("Overseas Engineer", London, November 1949)

Port Authority Builds Huge Steel Hangars at New York International Airport ("Civil Engineering", November 1949)

Space Frame ("Architects' Journal", London, October 24th 1946)

Aircraft Hangar for British European Airways ("Architects' Journal", London, May 1st 1947)

REINFORCED CONCRETE

Concrete—Dr. K. Hajnal-Kónyi ("New Ways of Building", The Architectural Press, London, 1948)

Three Articles on South American Building—A. J. Boase ("Engineering News-Record", October 19th 1944, April 19th and June 28th, 1945)

Concrete Building Design Trend Shaped by Clear Space Needs—A. J. Boase ("Engineering News-Record", October 18th 1945)

Some Long Time Tests on Concrete—M. O. Withey and K. F. Wendt ("Journal of the American Concrete Institute", February 1943)

Survey of Concrete in Building Design—A. J. Boase ("Architectural Record", October 1939)

New Ways to Save Steel in Concrete ("Architectural Record", February 1942)

Effect of Type of Bar on Width of Cracks in Reinforced Concrete Subjected to Tension—D. Watstein and N. A. Seese Jr. ("Journal of the American Concrete Institute", February 1945)

Structural Pre-cast Reinforced Concrete—K. Billig (Paper read to the Institution of Civil Engineers, March 1947—Cement and Concrete Association, London)

Design of Pre-cast Reinforced Concrete Frames ("Concrete and Constructional Engineering", London, November 1946)

A New System for Pre-cast Concrete Frames ("Architects' Journal", London, March 21st 1946)

Cemenstone Pre-cast Construction—A. C. Grafflin ("Journal of the American Concrete Institute", November 1948)

Navy Storehouse Built of Prefabricated Concrete Parts—A. Amirikian ("Journal of the American Concrete Institute", June 1947)

Prefabrication of Multi-storey Buildings ("Building", London, April 1947)

Shell Concrete Construction—H. G. Cousins (Paper read to the Reinforced Concrete Association, London, January 1948)

Shell Construction—Ove Arup ("Architectural Design", London, November 1947)

Shell Concrete Construction—K. Hajnal-Kónyi ("Architects' Journal", London, September 21st 1944)

Concert Hall, Broadcasting Centre, Copenhagen ("Architectural Forum", June 1947)

Wythenshawe Bus Garage ("The Builder", London, July 19th 1946)

Big Bomber Repair Hangar Sets New World Size Record—Raymond P. Day ("Contractors and Engineers Monthly", November 1948)

Buildings at Filton for the British Overseas Airways Corporation ("Concrete and Constructional Engineering", London, July 1949)

Hyperbolic-Paraboloid Concrete Roofs in Czechoslovakia—Prof. K. Hruban ("Concrete and Constructional Engineering", London, August 1949)

Pre-stressed Reinforced Concrete—K. Billig (Paper read to the Reinforced Concrete Association, London, October 1946)

Fully and Partly Pre-stressed Reinforced Concrete—P. W. Abeles ("Journal of the American Concrete Institute", January and November 1945)

Pre-stressed Reinforced Concrete—Dr. K. Hajnal-Kónyi ("Architects' Journal", London, May 6th 1943)

Pre-stressed Reinforced Concrete Hangar at the Civil Airport of Karachi—C. G. Sexton ("Journal of the Institution of Civil Engineers", December 1947)

Pre-stressed Bridge at Luzancy ("Travaux", Paris, August 1946 and January 1949)

Diversité des Applications du Béton Précontraint—M. Lalande ("Travaux", Paris, January and February 1949)

Vacuum Processes Applied to Pre-cast Concrete Houses—K. P. Billner and B. M. Thorud ("Journal of the American Concrete Institute", October 1949)

New Construction Technique Reduces Cost of Large-scale Housing in New York—John P. Riley ("Civil Engineering", May 1947)

Why Slab-band Floors are Economical—F. N. Severud ("Engineering News-Record," October 17th 1946)

Construction of the Sandö Bridges, Sweden—S. Klingberg ("Highways, Bridges and Aerodromes", England, October 20th 1948)

Two Hangars near Rome ("The Architect and Building News", London, August 26th 1949)

Extensions, Boots Factory, Beeston ("Architects' Journal", London, December 29th 1938)

Empire Pool, Wembley ("Architectural Review", London, September 1934)

Flats at Rosebery Avenue, London ("Architects' Journal", London, September 12th 1946)

Flats at Highgate, London ("The Architect and Building News", London, January 10th 1936)

Timber—P. O. Reece ("New Ways of Building", The Architectural Press, London, 1948)

TIMBER

Wood as an Engineering Material—L. J. Markwardt ("Proceedings of the American Society for Testing Materials", June 1943)

Revival of Wood as a Building Material—Don Taylor ("Architectural Record", December 1939)

Wood Structural Research and Development—Report prepared by the Field Information Agency, Technical United States Group Control Council for Germany. (Final Report No. 225, October 1945)

Modern Timber Structures of the Swiss Federal Railways—O. Wichser ("Schweizerische Bauzeitung", Nos. 2 to 4, January 1946)

Recent Experience in the Design of Timber Structures—P. O. Reece ("Journal of the Royal Institute of British Architects", March 1944)

Strength and Beauty from the Woods—V. Ketchum ("Western Construction News", July and August 1949)

War-time Innovations in Timber Design—Albert G. H. Dietz ("Engineering News-Record" October 18th 1945)

The Glued Laminated Wooden Arch—T. R. C. Wilson ("Forest Products Technical Bulletin" No. 691, U. S. Dept. of Agriculture, 1939)

Timber-Connector Joints: Their Strength and Design—J. A. Scholten ("Forest Products Technical Bulletin" No. 865, U. S. Dept. of Agriculture, 1944)

Synthetic Resin Glues ("Forest Products Report" No. 1336, U. S. Dept. of Agriculture, 1945)

Timber Hangar's Collapse in Florida Hurricane Investigated—D. E. Carberry ("Civil Engineering", September 1946)

Aircraft Plant has 150 ft. Timber Trusses ("Engineering News-Record", October 21st 1943)

Prefabricated Timber Factory ("Architectural Forum" September 1947)

Pioneer Design in Laminated Wood I-Beams—S. B. Barnes ("Engineering News-Record", February 22nd 1945)

Long-Span Arches for Modification Center ("Engineering News-Record", October 21st 1943)

How and When to use Aluminium Alloys—R. L. Moore ("Engineering News-Record", October 18th 1945)

ALUMINIUM ALLOYS

The Application of Light Aluminium Alloys to Structural Engineering—D. V. Pike ("The Structural Engineer", London, July 1945)

Aluminium Alloys: Some Possible Applications in Building—Dr. E. G. West (Paper read to the Incorporated Association of Architects and Surveyors, England, June 14th 1944; reported in "Architects' Journal", London, July 7th 1944)

Light Metals—P. Scholberg ("New Ways of Building", The Architectural Press, London, 1948)

Index